STORIES FOR THE SAKE OF ARGUMENT

Stories to get you arguing with your family, friends, and community. And that's a good thing!

ROBBIE GRINGRAS & ABI DAUBER STERNE

ISBN 979-8-9852495-0-7

Printed in the United States of America by FSA Publications 2022

FSA Publications
29 Barberry Ln.
Williamsville, NY 14221

Book design: Verticalloop

inquiries@forthesakeofargument.org

Written by Robbie Gringras and Abi Dauber Sterne with the generous support of the Jewish Agency for Israel, and the Jim Joseph Foundation.

Educators! If you use a story with your learners, why don't you encourage them to take the story home to use with their family or friends? You can download a PDF for each of the stories in this book by visiting forthesakeofargument.org/download and selecting the story (or stories) you want in a digital format. The passcode is the page number with the title "Tips for leading a healthy argument with a group". Enjoy!

ACKNOWLEDGMENTS

We would like to thank the Jim Joseph Foundation for their belief, support, and flexibility. They saw the potential of our work as the COVID-19 pandemic forced a pivot, and we will be forever grateful. Our work with the Moishe House organization, and in particular with its two stars, Roey Kruvi and Meghan Rodarte, sparked the thinking and exploration behind arguments that led us to *Stories for the Sake of Argument*. We also owe a significant debt of gratitude to the Jewish Agency for Israel, who acted as the incubator for all our work in Israel education through argument and in our writing the book itself.

Many thanks in all humility to those we learned from—through reading and through listening. The following thinkers and practitioners were wonderfully generous with their time: Toni Boyd, Lauren Cohen Fisher, Keren Fraiman, Dr. Alick Isaacs, Rabbi Dr. Daniel Roth, Leah Solomon, and Rabbi Melissa Weintraub, to name but a few. Although we never spoke directly to them, the following writers and thinkers spoke directly to us and to our work: Jonathan Haidt, Keith Kahn-Harris, Ian Leslie, Yascha Mounck, Priya Parker, Bruno Latour, Sherry Turkle, and Theodore Zeldin. We owe a huge debt to their writing, but our initial inspiration came from Joel Grishaver's *You Be the Judge*—a dilemmas book that saved Abi's family dinner table many times during lockdown!

Help and encouragement has been in abundance from family, friends, and colleagues. Special thanks go to Abi's mother, Antoinette Dauber, whose sharp eye recognized potential in our early stories. Thanks also to Cynthia Tzvibel-Navon's crucial support; Gila Orkin's PR wizardry; Fern Reiss' sage advice; Clive Gringras' generous wisdom; Kalela Lancaster's organizational philosophy; Nadav Nachmani's fantastic animations; TheWriteEdit.com's editing; and the wondrous design work of all the amazing women at Verticalloop.

Final thanks to our respective spouses, Dorit and Abe. Your constructive advice, creative ideas, and endless support have been the beating heart of all our endeavors.

INTRODUCTION

This is not your usual storybook.

First, we do not encourage you to curl up in a comfortable chair and read it to yourself. Quite the opposite. We encourage you to read these stories out loud to your family or to a group of friends. Don't keep them to yourself.

Second, we do not expect you and your friends to smile beatifically and silently at some lovely turn of phrase. Instead, we hope the stories will provoke you into an argument. Yes, that's right. "Argument" has become a harsh word, but it didn't always resonate with fears of violence and irreparable damage. Once upon a time (at the risk of beginning another story!) we would argue in order to get smarter, to get to know each other better, to understand the world more clearly and not just focus on ourselves and our own ideas. This storybook is here to help you rehabilitate and reclaim arguments for a better world.

Every one of the stories in this book is written with a disagreement in mind. Each story presents a clash of values that cannot be avoided. You are asked to take a side—even if you find yourself taking a side you wouldn't ordinarily favor. This is the fun of values clashes: they reveal how our principles cannot always save us from having to make independent choices in the moment. Sometimes we surprise ourselves pleasantly when we have to rely on our inconsistent yet authentic humanity as well as our ideals.

Third, this is a storybook that is also an exercise book. It is a personal trainer. We believe that we all need to develop our argument muscles. We need to build up our disagreement stamina. Our world requires more of us to venture into the discomfort of disagreement, so as to begin to build bridges of humanity with those whose opinions we vehemently reject.

This exercise book does not call for consensus or surrender; it hopes to train us all to be brave enough to disagree with those we disagree with, and not just share our disgust for their views with our supporters. If you are reading this book within a family, it's an excellent lesson for your kids. And if you're working with this book in an educational setting, the importance of this challenge is even greater.

Finally, you will notice that all the stories directly or indirectly involve Israel. Mainly, this is because the two of us live in Israel! It is a country in which we have chosen to live and raise our (arguing) families, and we find this place endlessly fascinating, dynamic, and meaningful. The second reason is because we both work in Israel education, and we firmly believe that no learning about Israel can happen without an argument. Israel is a living embodiment of several ongoing, interlocking arguments, and the most effective and honest way of learning about Israel's arguments is by empowering the learner to join in. But more important than our personal commitments or profession is our belief that Israel's local arguments are the arguments of the world. Only louder.

Arguments over race. Arguments between personal conscience and public decree. Arguments about power and force. About East and West. About land and resources. About democratic rights. All these arguments rage across the world and find particular salience in Israel.

We hope you enjoy *Stories for the Sake of Argument.*

Robbie Gringras and Abi Dauber Sterne

(At the end of the book you'll also find a few tips for running an "Argument Circle" for friends and for families.)

How to Read this Book

You are of course completely welcome to read this book from cover to cover. However, if you do intend to read the stories out loud to your family, friends, or learners, here are a couple of pointers:

Story types

You'll see there are three different labels for different kinds of stories.

WARM-UPS

The warm-up label means that this story is what we might call "low stakes." Little knowledge is required to discuss the story's challenges, and the world will not change depending on what decisions are made. It might be a story you would read with younger participants, or a story you might use as a "warm-up" to hotter topics.

ISRAEL

The "Israel" label means that this story deals directly and specifically with issues in Israel. The values behind the argument are still universal and accessible to all, but the subject matter is specific to Israel.

ALLEGORY

The allegory label means that this story can be read on two levels. A fruitful and passionate discussion can draw its energy from the straightforward situation represented by the story. But you can also add in—perhaps after the initial argument—the real-life dilemma that this story is allegorizing. This can lead to another new level of argument.

Background and guiding questions

Following every story is a set of guiding questions and some background material about the story itself.

BACKGROUND

Sometimes the background texts offer information about real-life situations the story is based on. Sometimes they point to their allegorical nature, and sometimes they provide a broader moral context within which to make your judgments. You can read them out loud to your group or family, and you can simply read them to yourself.

GUIDING QUESTIONS

We provide two sets of guiding questions. The first set is to open up discussion and disagreement about the story itself and the characters' choices. The second set encourages a broader, more universal discussion about how these specific decisions point to a larger global issue.

Table of Contents

Every argument that is for the sake of Heaven, it is destined to endure. But if it is not for the sake of heaven -- it is not destined to endure. . . . And with the argument which is for the sake of Heaven, the purpose and aim that is sought from that argument is to arrive at the truth, and this endures. . . . And with the argument which is not for the sake of Heaven, its desired purpose is to achieve power and the love of contention, and its end will not endure.

- Talmud Avot 5:17

Monstrosities

Grandpa actively ignores someone who he says supports "mass murder." Should the grandchild ignore him too?

We've placed this story first, as it addresses a key challenge of our age: What are the costs of choosing not to argue and instead choosing to shun?

I'd never seen Grandpa so angry. And at temple, of all places. It was the strangest thing.

At first, I couldn't even understand what had happened. As usual, we were lining up to shake hands with the Rabbi and the congregation's president. Grandpa shook hands with the Rabbi and thanked her for the sermon, but then stopped short when he came to the president, Jack Levy. Jack put out his hand, and Grandpa just looked at him with death in his eyes, a pale-white face, and snarled, "No way in hell I'm going to shake your hand." And he stormed off.

I had to run to catch up with him, as he was already getting his coat, ready to walk home on his own.

"Grandpa! What did President Jack do to you? What did he do?" I shouted in surprise and concern. "Did he say something bad to Grandma?"

"He's a mass murderer," muttered Grandpa.

"What?! President Jack is a m—"

Grandpa cut me off. "He's not a mass murderer himself. But he supports one. There are thousands getting killed every day, and he doesn't care. The actual president, the president of our country, could stop these murders whenever he wants. But he doesn't. He lets them carry on. And Jack"—Grandpa almost spat out the name—"Jack Levy supports him."

I was a little disappointed. "And that's why you won't shake his hand?"

Grandpa nodded.

"Just because he supports the president?"

"It's not 'just.' It's everything," replied Grandpa. "How can I be friendly with someone who is completely fine with monstrosities? If someone's not bothered by monstrosities, then they're a monster themselves. And I would be one too, if I behaved as if it didn't matter."

"So," I worried out loud, "if President Levy, I mean Jack, gives me a candy, should I give it back?"

Grandpa stood there for a second, hesitating before answering.

The candy burned in my pocket as I waited for the reply.

GUIDING QUESTIONS

- Is Grandpa right to shun Jack Levy?

- Should Grandpa try to engage Jack in a conversation? Why? Why not?

- Should Grandpa tell his grandchild to refuse Jack's candies?

- And if he does so, should the grandchild return the candy?

- What was the "mass murder" you imagined Grandpa to be protesting?

- If the "mass murder" Grandpa perceives was due to abortion, would any of your views change?

BACKGROUND

Grandpa is enforcing a personal form of shunning for what he believes are the best most moral reasons possible. Interestingly enough, shunning is a practice that Jews traditionally enacted.

Shunning in Jewish tradition

The Rambam (Maimonides, the great twelfth century rabbinic scholar), provides us with twenty-four reasons why a community member might be shunned and is also quite specific as to what shunning entails: a month in social isolation while speaking with no one, and an expectation to behave and dress as if in mourning. (*Moed Katan*, 16a)

It seems that the difference between the tradition of *nidui* (shunning) and Grandpa's actions is that shunning was always decided upon by the ruling authority over the community. A group of people whom the entire community respects came together to decide whether to apply this punishment.

Nowadays it is difficult to clarify where one's community begins and ends, and who are the people the entire community respects enough to give them such authority?

Shunning and the candy

In a sense, this is why the question of the candy is so important.

When Grandpa refuses to relate to Jack, that's an individual choice. Were Grandpa to tell his grandchild to refuse Jack's candies, that would no longer be an individual gesture, but rather a *nidui*. Grandpa would be using his authority over his grandchild to widen the circle of those who shun Jack.

 QUESTIONS FOR FURTHER EXPLORATION

- Is it okay to shun someone for actions you believe to be monstrous?

- When should you engage in discussion with someone even if you believe their actions are monstrous?

- Is it okay to encourage others to shun someone for actions you believe to be monstrous?

- What would you classify as "monstrous" actions that might be worthy of mass shunning?

- What would you classify as awful behavior, but not worthy of shunning?

- Can you imagine how someone with vastly different values from yours might see any of your actions or beliefs as monstrous?

 # THOUGHTS TO RETURN TO AFTER A NIGHT'S SLEEP

1   I wish I'd said ...

2   That idea I rejected, now that I think about it ...

3   That whole conversation reminded me of ...

"THE AIM OF ARGUMENT, OR OF DISCUSSION, should not be victory, BUT PROGRESS."

— Joseph Joubert

THE JEWISH SOUL YEARNS

> The Arab captain of Israel's national soccer team does not sing "Hatikvah," the national anthem. A fan has a problem with that …

I can honestly say that it was one of the most moving experiences of my life. There we were, all together in the stadium for the first time since COVID, roaring our hearts out together in pride and excitement at the start of the game. Singing "Hatikvah," the national anthem, has always been important for me. My mother was among the Holocaust survivors who sang "Hatikvah" for the BBC when the people in the concentration camps were liberated in 1945. And here we were, in totally different circumstances, singing the national anthem of our state, at the beginning of a game that could get us into the World Cup finals for the first time in fifty years!

More than that, I was so proud of my team and my country. Our captain was Abu Sayid, one of the best center backs in the league. He's an Arab guy who plays for Bnei Sakhnin, and he scored the winning goal three weeks ago, which put us within touching distance of the World Cup finals! I was hoarse for days after screaming his name. For me, the fact that Abu Sayid was captain says all you need to know about my country: if you're the best, you'll rise to the top irrespective of whether you're Jew or Arab. We're all Israelis here, and we're going to the World Cup finals!

I was celebrating all night. But the following morning a clip was doing the rounds. Abu Sayid had given an interview straight after the game.

"So, how does it feel to qualify for the World Cup finals as your country's captain?" asked the interviewer.

"Fantastic," replied Abu Sayid.

"So if you're so proud to lead Israel to the World Cup finals, why didn't you sing 'Hatikvah' at the start of the game?" The TV cut to a clip of the start of the game, where you could see Abu Sayid in the lineup, mouth closed, looking straight ahead, while everyone else was singing 'Hatikvah.' It was plain as day.

Abu Sayid didn't flinch.

"I don't sing your 'Hatikvah.' It's not my anthem."

Before the interviewer could recover from his shock, Abu Sayid calmly quoted the lyrics: "The Jewish soul yearns. . . . An eye gazes toward Zion. Our hope is not yet lost. . . . to be a free people in our land . . ." and continued with a shrug, "What can you do? I'm a proud Israeli, but I don't have a Jewish soul. I don't see my land as Zion. It's the truth. So I give you respect, I stand with my team while they sing, but me, I don't sing." And then he strolled off to join his celebrating teammates.

I hit the roof. How dare he! The captain of our national team rejects the national anthem? What, he's going to go to the World Cup finals and shame the entire nation before the eyes of the world? The song that my mother sang to keep herself alive in the concentration camps is too good for him? The words are suddenly so important to him? Does everyone in England truly want God to save the Queen?

This man cannot be the captain of our national team.

And that's why I'm here at the demonstrations every night. We're demanding that Abu Sayid be removed as captain. The captain of Israel's national team is the representative of Israel. And Abu Sayid clearly does not want to represent Israel. Some of the guys here don't even want him to play on the team at all. I say we should let him play, but he can't be the captain.

Do you understand me?

 # GUIDING QUESTIONS

- What do you think of Abu Sayid's opinion? What do you think of the demonstrators?

- Does Abu Sayid's protest against singing "Hatikvah" make him unsuitable to represent Israel?

- Should Abu Sayid be removed as captain of the Israeli soccer team? Should he be allowed to stay on as a player but not as the captain?

 # BACKGROUND

Incidents like the one described in this story arise every few years in Israel. Rifaat Turk, the first Arab to play for Israel's national soccer team, refused to sing "Hatikvah" in 1976.

In a 2015 interview, a Muslim-Israeli soccer player and captain of the Israeli national team, Bibras Natkho, explained why he, too, does not sing the anthem. "The team and the country are very important to me, but I'm Muslim and so I can't sing some of the words," said Natkho. "I can't sing the anthem without feeling like a part of it, and that comes out of a great respect for it. I feel a great sense of belonging to the team and the country."

Eyal Berkovic, a soccer player who was a candidate to become coach of the Israeli national team, said in response, "I appreciate Bibras as a player who gives everything out on the field. He's a great player and I appreciate and love him, but in my opinion, Bibras, you cannot be captain if you don't sing the national anthem [. . .] for me, you can't have the captain of Israel's national team not sing the anthem."

In response, Natkho replied, "Sorry, Eyal, but to remind you, the State of Israel is home to non-Jewish people as well. I don't know if there's another country that speaks about religion in its anthem," adding that his father "served in the Israeli Border Police for thirty years. He served the country a lot more than many others, who, to put it gently, don't contribute anything."

Interestingly, recently in American professional football, the US anthem, "The Star-Spangled Banner," also became the center of a controversy. Black football players began "taking a knee" during the anthem, to protest historical treatment of African Americans in the country. The National Football League ultimately ruled that players must stand for the anthem. However, players who want to protest can recuse themselves by staying in the locker room until after the anthem is sung.

QUESTIONS FOR FURTHER EXPLORATION

- What does it mean to sing a national anthem? Does it mean something different to you than it does to those who differ from you?

- Should national symbols be eternal, never changing, "sacred," or should they change with the times? What are the advantages and disadvantages of both approaches?

- Are there situations in which you would insist on singing your national anthem? Are there situations in which you would refuse?

 ## THOUGHTS TO RETURN TO AFTER A NIGHT'S SLEEP

1 I wish I'd said ...

2 That idea I rejected, now that I think about it ...

3 That whole conversation reminded me of ...

THE BROTHERS' HOUSE

Jonny lives in the family house, while David lives abroad. Is it okay for David to criticize what Jonny does with their house?

Once upon a time there were two brothers, Jonny and David. As children they loved playing in their family home. Time passed, as time does, and the boys grew up. Their parents aged, and eventually the time came for the boys to bury their father, and then some years later, their mother.

David got a job abroad. The brothers agreed that Jonny would live in their family home, and would always keep David's room available for his occasional visits. In the meantime Jonny kept up the house, fixing things that needed fixing, dealing with things that needed to be dealt with, while David would send money to cover his half of the costs.

One day, many years later, David came for a visit. Jonny was delighted. Together the two of them opened up David's room and cleared away the cobwebs. They were together again in their home, if only for a short time.

But things had changed. Since David's last visit, Jonny had become more religiously observant, and now the whole kitchen had separate areas for meat and milk. There were two ovens, two sinks, and different cutlery and plates for each of them. David didn't have a problem with religion per se, but it was kind of irritating having to suddenly be careful about what food he brought into what was, after all, his house.

More troubling was the garden outside. It had once been an open, grassy area that all the neighborhood houses backed up to. All the kids would play together in its weeds and puddles. But now the garden was a beautiful green lawn, trimmed and carefully cultivated with flowers around the edges, all completely fenced in.

"What's the fence for?" wailed David when he first saw it. "It was so wonderful when everything was open to all the neighbors!"

"Yes," acknowledged Jonny, "but the neighbors are different now. I know we were friends with them when we were kids, but it's their children who live there now, and they are monsters. There've been break-ins and vandalism. There was no choice but to put up the fences. And besides," he said, gesturing proudly, "isn't it beautiful now?"

David grunted.

"What is your problem?" shouted Jonny. "You've been away for years while I've dealt with everything in this house. What right do you have to criticize?"

"Because it's my house too!"

"But I live here. All the time! You don't like the way I do things here? Come back and move in permanently. Then we can talk about 'our' house!"

"The more time I spend in 'your' house, the less I want anything to do with it," shot back David.

The huge argument had only just begun.

GUIDING QUESTIONS

- Is David wrong to criticize Jonny when he does not even live in the house?

- Should Jonny allow David to veto the changes he wants to make to the house?

BACKGROUND

This story can be understood as an allegory for the relationship between the Jews around the world and Israeli Jewry. It was inspired by Rabbi Shira Koch Epstein, who wanted to explain how she understood the relationship between Jews in the Diaspora and Jews in Israel. She described the relationship as one of siblings who have inherited their parents' house. The story is an allegorical expansion of that image.

In this narrative, we can imagine Jonny as representing Israeli Jews living in the shared "house" of Israel, and David as representing Diaspora Jewry living abroad. The Israeli Jonny is involved in the day-to-day upkeep of a house that he perceives to be located in an increasingly problematic neighborhood. The Diasporic David gives support from a distance, and occasionally visits.

Tensions arise between the "siblings" over three key areas:

• Mostly non-Orthodox Diaspora Jewry perceives Israel to be more and more religiously Orthodox, and feels uncomfortable with what it sees to be uncompromising attitudes toward the non-Orthodox. Clashes over women's prayer at the Kotel and conversion laws are the largest symbols of this discomfort.

• Mostly left-leaning Diaspora Jewry tends to disapprove of the way in which Israel relates to its Palestinian neighbors.

• Diaspora Jewry can express frustration at the way in which Israel makes alterations to the nature of the state without consulting or communicating with Diaspora Jewry.

For their part, many Israelis can be confounded and even insulted by Diaspora-born progressive forms of Judaism. What they see as life-and-death responses to dangerous "neighbors" are not respected by their distant and secure "siblings." And while Israelis constantly maintain the open invitation of immediate immigration (through the Law of Return) to their Diaspora family, they often feel their siblings prefer to criticize from a distance.

How does the story read to you now, with this interpretation in your mind?

QUESTIONS FOR FURTHER EXPLORATION

- Do Diaspora Jews sometimes feel that Israeli actions affect the way others relate to them personally? And does that give them more right to criticize?

- What are the rights and obligations of Diaspora Jews? Should they be allowed a vote in Israeli elections? Should they serve in the Israeli army?

- Should Israel consult with the Diaspora on issues that impact them?

 # THOUGHTS TO RETURN TO AFTER A NIGHT'S SLEEP

1 I wish I'd said ...

2 That idea I rejected, now that I think about it ...

3 That whole conversation reminded me of ...

"THE DIFFICULT PART
IN AN ARGUMENT IS
not to defend one's
opinion but rather
TO KNOW IT."

– ANDRE MAUROIS

THE GOOD MAN

An orthodox Jew raises money for his wonderful charity and finds himself at odds with those who dislike his all-male fundraiser.

There was once a good man. A religious man. An orthodox man.

He spent his entire life helping sick people receive the medical treatment they needed.

He didn't care if they were good people or bad people. He didn't care if they were men or women, Jewish or Muslim, religious or secular. He looked after anyone who needed help because he saw this was what he had to do, as a religious man.

One day he began organizing his annual fundraising event and succeeded in getting all sorts of pop stars to perform on stage. Lots of pop stars meant lots of donations. Lots of donations meant even more sick people receiving the care they required.

The good man was delighted. Publicity was sent out far and wide.

But with the publicity out, all could see that every artist on the bill was a man. It was almost as if women were being kept off the stage deliberately. It turned out that they were. The good man was a religious man, an orthodox man, and just as his orthodox values led him to blessed charity work, his values also held that women should not sing in front of men.

Everyone told the good man that he could not have a public event that refused to let any women on stage. It would be like saying that women don't matter.

But the good man's supporters knew it would be crazy to expect him to ignore his religious beliefs when raising money for a charity built on those beliefs.

Gradually, one by one, the artists began pulling out of the event. They said they were happy to perform, but only if women could perform too. But the good man could not agree to host an event that undermined his own values.

Everything was resting on a knife-edge.

Would an event take place that consciously and deliberately excluded women? Or, alternatively, would the event be cancelled, ensuring that far fewer people would be helped by the man who wished to help them?

GUIDING QUESTIONS

- How do you think the story should best and most realistically end?

- If you had the Good Man's ear, what would you say to him?

- If you had the ear of one of the pop stars invited to perform, what would you say to him?

- If the event were to go ahead, with only men on the stage and with all earnings donated to the amazing work of the organization, would you yourself buy a ticket to the event?

BACKGROUND

This refers to a true story about Rabbi Elimelech Firer and his organization "Ezra LeMarpe—Help Towards Healing." In November 2019 his fundraising concert in Tel Aviv that would have refused a platform to women was indeed canceled after public uproar.

At the time there were many artists, including many women, who were outraged about the cancellation of Firer's event. Margalit Tzan'ani, an Israeli female singer and TV personality, commented, "Of course I'm against the exclusion of women, but let's be clear: what's more important? The huge, wonderful acts of kindness of Rav Firer, a unique genius, or one particular show where women won't perform?"

The education minister at the time, himself an Orthodox religious man, complained: "A man who aided and contributed so much to Israel's sick, suffers a media bulldozer and a campaign against the show in his honor, and all this because of his way of life."

On the other side, journalist and TV presenter Einav Galili expressed her outrage at the exclusion of women ironically. "I find it so moving when men, despite the difficulties involved, are willing to swallow their pride, bite their lips, and give up on my rights," she said. This is not the only public event in Israel that does not allow women on stage. The official lighting of the Chanukah candles at the Kotel excludes women, and in the fall of 2019 there was even an event for the Empowerment of Women in Ramla . . . with no women on stage.

 # QUESTIONS FOR FURTHER EXPLORATION

Do any of these statements resonate with you?

• "A just society must leave room for all groups to enact their own beliefs and customs."

• "Helping the sick is more important than always giving women a platform."

• "Women must never be excluded from public life just because they are women."

• "Compromising on your values is tantamount to denying who you are."

THOUGHTS TO RETURN TO AFTER A NIGHT'S SLEEP

1 I wish I'd said ...

2 That idea I rejected, now that I think about it ...

3 That whole conversation reminded me of ...

"THE ETYMOLOGY OF THE WORD 'ARGUE' TIES BACK TO THE LATIN WORD FOR ILLUMINATE, so that's what we should do. SHINE A LIGHT ON DIFFERENCE and argue."

– REV. ZINA JACQUE

Musica Cubana

A private social club for Cuban expats suddenly has to cope with non-Cubans wishing to participate.

Look, they can call it mambo or salsa or cha-cha, but as far as I'm concerned, they're all just names to explain it to Americans. To me it's all got one name: Cuban music. That was the idea for the club. A private members-only club simply called Musica Cubana. A place where old Cubans could gather once a week to listen to our old music, drink Cuban drinks, eat Cuban food, and talk Cuban Spanish without having to "translate" it to anyone else.

We didn't advertise all that much; we just went *boca a boca* (word of mouth), and within six months we were filling the club every Thursday night. After a year or two we were able to buy our own place, all paid for by members' dues.

I can't tell you how much I used to look forward to my evenings at Musica Cubana. It wasn't just the music or the food. It was that feeling of home. Old friends, old guys who looked like they were old friends, and the chatter. Loud chatter in Cuban Spanish. Yes, that's right, not your mainland Spanish, but our Spanish. With our accents, and our soft "s." Slang, curses, laughter, jokes—all Cuban.

I don't know about you, but my English is not so great. I can write fine, but when I have to speak it I clam up. Even Luis, who teaches English literature at a college somewhere, even he has a heavy accent in English and still expresses himself better in Cuban. The moment you'd open the door to Musica Cubana your guard would come down, and the Cuban hidden inside would just bubble over. It was such a beautiful feeling.

And there was the small stuff that you don't talk about but you can just feel in your bones. Like the rice and beans that Ernesto serves. Tastes dreadful. But I don't care because Ernesto calls it by its Cuban name: *Moros y Cristianos*. Not only that, but he says it with a wink, so you know he understands that the name refers to the ancient Spanish rivalry between the Moors of North Africa and the European Christians, and how their different-colored skins mirror the contrast between white rice and black beans. Eating Ernesto's Moros y Cristianos is a stomach-churning affair. Lord knows how he ended up being a cook! But it still feels like a deep mouthful of home.

Musica Cubana was my second home. My heart's home, if you want the truth. I love my wife and my kids, but hanging at Musica Cubana was like being weightless. No effort to speak in English (Maria insists we speak English with the kids, and I get it), no need to explain anything, no need for anything to be explained to me. Until the Guests arrived.

It started with only one or two. A few of the younger guys started turning up with their girlfriends. American girlfriends. Not Cuban. That's okay, I'm happy for them. Maria is from Mexico, and we've been married for over thirty years. But I don't bring her to the club. The club is for Cubans.

Not only that, these guests, they don't speak Spanish. That's okay too. But now, if you're sitting at a table with these folks, all of a sudden it's rude to speak in Spanish. They wouldn't be able to understand. At Musica Cubana suddenly I have to speak in English.

Soon enough the number of guests starts to rise. More and more gringos and gringas, needing translations. Got to be inclusive, man, they tell me. They tell me we got to change the signs on the bathrooms because now not everyone understands the Spanish. It's crazy. It's getting like I don't recognize the place anymore.

Now they want to let these guests become members, say it's not fair they come every week but have to pay guest prices every time. They want to pay membership dues like everyone else. I'm okay with that. I don't want to exploit anybody. You come here regularly, you should get equal rights.

Only thing is, once you're a member, you get to vote in the Annual General Meeting. You get to have a say about what music we play, what food we eat, what language we speak in the club.

So what happens when they become the majority? What happens when they want to play American rap instead of Compay Segundo and Ñico Saquito? I'll go crazy!

I say there has to be a limit. That if Musica Cubana is to remain the club it was always meant to be—a refuge for the weary Cuban soul—there has to be a limit.

They want to be members? Fine. Want to vote in the Annual General Meeting and influence what goes on here? Fine. Make them full members.

But I just say we should put a limit on the numbers. I say the membership of Musica Cubana should always be at least 80 percent Cuban.

They want a different kind of club, let them set it up for themselves.

Do you understand me?

GUIDING QUESTIONS

- Do you understand where he is coming from?

- Do you agree with his suggestion to limit the number of non-Cubans at the club?

- If you were a member of the club, would you think differently?

- Should the club simply refuse entrance to anyone who is not Cuban? And if it were to do so, does this suggest the club members see themselves as better than the non-Cubans?

BACKGROUND

Some may say that this story is analogous to the immigration policy of the State of Israel. In the state of the Jews, automatic citizenship is granted to any Jew who wishes to immigrate. This is a right that is only granted to Jews. The argument is that to maintain Israel as the "refuge for the weary [Jewish] soul," it must maintain a clear Jewish majority. In this analogy, Jews are seen as the Cuban "members of the club," and the others are "guests." The analogy is of course not exact.

Others may see that the story is analogous to the Palestinian responses to Jewish immigration in the early twentieth century. There was significant opposition to Jewish immigration through protest, lobbying, and violence. At that time the Palestinians might be seen as the "club members" and the Jews as the "guests." This analogy is also not exact.

Yet it would be fair to say the story speaks to immigration.

Every country in the world has immigration laws that limit the number of people entering their country, and each applies clear criteria for those wishing to gain citizenship. Some countries' criteria are specific: immigrants must invest in the country, or possess certain skills, or prove a familial, or ethnic, or historical connection. Some allow for a lottery system. Nearly all endeavor to place a limit on the final number of immigrants per year.

Some will argue that immigration must be limited because the host country has limited resources to support people. Some argue that unbridled immigration could be a security threat, and some—similar to our member of Musica Cubana—aim to maintain a certain cultural status quo. At the same time many argue that immigration brings with it innovative energy, economic growth, and cultural spice. All these arguments for either increasing or decreasing immigration have one assumption in common: there is such a thing as a "host" country with its own national interests, weighing what is good for itself and its current citizens.

QUESTIONS FOR FURTHER EXPLORATION

- Do you know how many immigrants your country allows each year?

- Do you believe that number is too high? Too low?

- Or do you believe national borders are entirely wrong, and all should be free to move and live where they want?

- What is the value in having exclusive organizations? Women's-only colleges, Black-only clubs, Jewish-only community centers?

 # THOUGHTS TO RETURN TO AFTER A NIGHT'S SLEEP

1 I wish I'd said ...

2 That idea I rejected, now that I think about it ...

3 That whole conversation reminded me of ...

"I FIND I AM MUCH PROUDER OF THE VICTORY I OBTAIN OVER MYSELF, when, in the very ardor of dispute, I MAKE MYSELF SUBMIT TO MY ADVERSARY'S FORCE OF REASON, THAN I AM PLEASED WITH THE VICTORY I OBTAIN OVER HIM THROUGH HIS WEAKNESS."

- Michel de Montaigne -

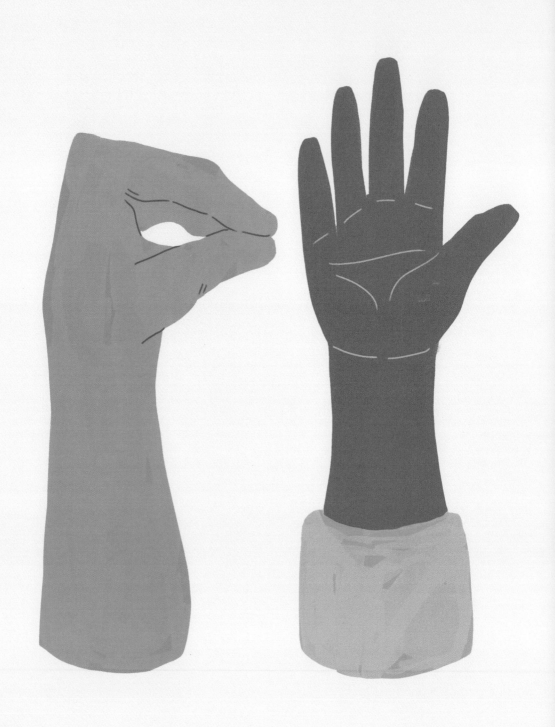

THAT'S JUST HOW IT IS

> Family decisions are always made by a vote. But what happens when someone new "joins" the family?

In my family we have a system.

Mom decides nearly everything: what time to get up to go to school, who has to throw out the garbage, which car to buy, and whether or not we can have a friend sleep over.

It's just how it is.

But for other stuff, we vote. Mom gives us all a vote—me, my three younger sisters, and my two older brothers. My sisters and I wanted to give Jack a vote too, but Mom said that dogs don't get to vote and that's just how it is.

Mom votes too, of course, but she's just one vote out of seven, so she doesn't always get her way. We vote on whether we can eat french fries, what color the new car is going to be, where the sofa should sit, and sometimes we even vote on what clothes Mom ought to wear when she goes out on a date.

It works pretty well. Especially when there's an argument, everyone gives way to the vote.

47

Except things have started to change lately, and I'm not sure I like it. Mom started going out with this guy Assim. He's nice enough, I guess. He's started hanging around here more and more, which my brothers like because he plays video games with them. But the problems began when we were all arguing about where to go on our family vacation. It was a pretty big deal and all, a big outlay and a whole week away together.

I wanted New Orleans, but others wanted Miami. Just as the volume started rising, and tempers started to fray, Mom did her usual: "Okay! A vote!" We all stopped shouting, kind of relieved the argument would be resolved one way or another. "Hands up, who wants New Orleans? And now hands up, who wants Miami?"

We all called it: "New Orleans! Four against three in favor of New Orleans! Yay!"

But then Assim kind of cleared his throat quietly and said, with this dumb smile on his face, "I think it's a tie, isn't it?"

And then we see that Assim is also holding his hand up, as if he were voting too.

There's this silence, like everyone's just taking a breath before jumping into a cold river, and then we all start shouting at once, "He doesn't get to vote!"

"Of course he gets to vote!"

"You're only saying that because you wanted Miami too!"

"What's he got to do with it?"

We all turn to look at Mom.

She takes a breath, and says carefully, "Well, I was hoping that Assim would come with us on this holiday . . . "

Another silence.

"And don't we get to vote on that?" I found myself blurting out. "No," said Mom. "No. Assim is coming with us. That's just how it is."

GUIDING QUESTIONS

- Should Assim get a vote? Why? Why not?

- Why would you say Mom is the one who decides on the issues that can be voted on and those that cannot?

- What do you think about this arrangement?

- How are/were decisions made in your family?

BACKGROUND

On the face of it, this story can be read as a tale of family management and the relationship between a single mother and her children. It can also be seen as an allegory for the nature of democracies throughout the world.

A crucial element of all democracies is not about how or why certain decisions are made. The more fundamental question is about who. Who are the people who are given a vote in elections, and who are not? Why is it that Mexicans or Canadians or Brits do not get a vote in USA elections?

The word "democracy" means literally, "the rule of the people." The people—in Greek, the demos—are those who make decisions about and for the demos, the people. Without a a mutually agreed group of people, there is no functioning democracy.

We give one vote only to every individual in our demos whom we trust to make decisions for the good of the demos.

There was a time in the United States when people of color were not seen to be part of the demos, and so had no right to vote. In most countries there was a time when women were not trusted to make responsible decisions, and were denied the right to vote. To this day certain countries will not allow felons to vote, and all countries deny the vote to who they define as children.

In order for a democracy to function, there must be a demos bound through mutual trust.

In a democracy, I agree to every single person in the demos having power equal to my own, in the shape of a single vote. Even if I disagree with their choices, I trust that they care about the country as much as I do and have an equal right to try to influence its decisions.

QUESTIONS FOR FURTHER EXPLORATION

- What does it mean to "trust" people you have never met?

- What might you require in order to "trust" people you have never met?

- Usually the way for an outsider to join the "demos" is by going through a process of becoming a citizen. What should be in that process that might bring you to trust them with a vote on your collective future?

 # THOUGHTS TO RETURN TO AFTER A NIGHT'S SLEEP

1   I wish I'd said ...

2   That idea I rejected, now that I think about it ...

3   That whole conversation reminded me of ...

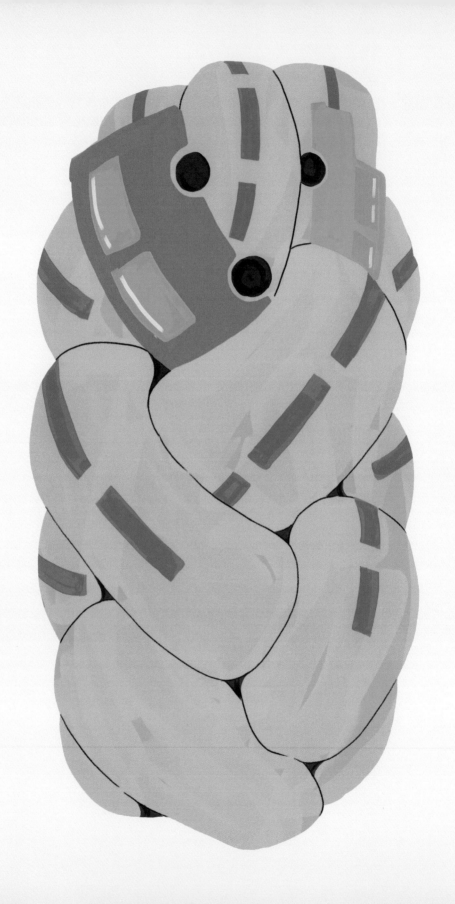

Shabbat Mornings with Savta

Her grandmother doesn't want her to come visit her on Shabbat by public transportation. She believes a Jewish state should not have buses running on the sabbath. But the granddaughter feels this is hypocritical.

Every Saturday morning, I push off that deep desire I have to stay in bed. I peel off my warm comforter, gingerly place my feet onto the cold tile floor, and get dressed quickly to visit my grandmother, Savta. Savta lives alone, on the other side of Haifa.

Aside from Saturday being a day off, it's also Shabbat. I don't do much by way of Shabbat, but Savta does. She keeps all the rules and all the customs. When I come to visit on Shabbat, Savta always serves her home-baked challah bread, and I make the *kiddush* blessing over sweet wine. Together, to Savta's great delight, we eat her old-style Jerusalem kugel. Every week we keep each other company, discuss whatever is on Savta's still-sharp mind, and touch the traditions that go back millennia.

One morning, Savta put down her cup of tea and announced, "I don't want you to take a bus to get to me on Shabbat anymore."

"What? You don't want me to visit?"

"Of course I want you to visit," Savta said, smiling. "But not on a public bus on Shabbat. There shouldn't even be a bus service on Shabbat. This country feels so much less Jewish than when I was a child. What is this country for if it doesn't feel Jewish? So please don't take buses to get to me on Shabbat anymore."

"But doesn't my visit to you on Shabbat make you feel Jewish?" I asked.

"It's what gives me personal pleasure. But it's not what makes the country feel Jewish. A country feels Jewish by how its public spaces look and feel. Of course, individuals should do what they want, but the country as a whole needs to preserve and strengthen its sense of Jewishness."

"So what does that mean? You want me to take a taxi to you on Shabbat instead?"

"Yes," said Savta.

"What, taxi drivers don't have to keep Shabbat?" I pressed.

"Taxi drivers are individuals who can decide their own personal practice, just like me and you. I don't mind you breaking Shabbat to get here. Your religiosity is your business. But buses are a government business, a public statement. Shutting down buses on Shabbat says something about the importance of national symbols of rest on Shabbat."

"Oh, Savta. I don't know. That feels like you're trying to have your kugel and eat it too. Either the country should impose rules for Shabbat or it shouldn't. Taxis okay but buses not? It sounds really inconsistent." I paused. "And, anyway, twenty percent of the country isn't Jewish. What about them?"

Savta pursed her lips.

"I've said what I have to say. You do with it what you want."

The conversation was over.

Both she and I knew that I would start taking taxis. I wasn't going to leave her all alone on Shabbat for the right to take public transportation. And besides, my taking a taxi wasn't going to change municipal policy overnight anyway.

But it didn't sit right with me. I knew this was going to be an ongoing disagreement between us for some time to come.

 ## GUIDING QUESTIONS

- Where would you come down on the disagreement?

- Do you agree with Savta or with her granddaughter?

- If you believe there should be public transportation in Israel on Shabbat, do you think there is anything Israel should do that would mark Shabbat as different from the rest of the week?

# BACKGROUND

It is significant that this story takes place in Haifa. Haifa is the only city in Israel where public transportation does run on the Jewish Sabbath. All other cities close down their buses and trains from Friday afternoon until late Saturday. For anyone spending Shabbat in Jerusalem or Tel Aviv, there is a marked difference in the atmosphere of a modern city, where most shops are closed and where no buses roar along the streets. In Haifa public transportation is less frequent on Shabbat than on other days of the week, but is still very much present.

At the end of this story the granddaughter mentions that around one out of every five Israelis in the country is not Jewish. Most are Muslim, and a minority are Christian or Druse. Their day of rest is Friday or Sunday, and tends to be marked by fewer restrictions in the public sphere. Fourteen percent of Haifa's residents are Christian Arab, and around four percent are Muslim Arab. One quarter of Haifa residents are Jewish immigrants from Russia, who tend not to observe an orthodox Shabbat.

The fact that most places in Israel do not run public transportation harkens back to an agreement that David Ben-Gurion came to with the ultra-Orthodox World Agudat Israel Organization in 1947. This was one year before the establishment of the State of Israel, and the UN was investigating the kind of state that the Zionists might create. As Ben-Gurion wrote in his introduction to the agreement letter: "The approval of the United Nations ... will not be possible unless the state provides freedom of conscience for all its citizens and makes it clear we have no intention of establishing a theocratic state. The Jewish state will also have non-Jewish citizens—Christians and Muslims—and full equal rights for all citizens and the absence of coercion and discrimination in religious affairs must be guaranteed in advance." As part of this agreement, all sides agreed that "the legal day of rest in the Jewish state will be Saturday, obviously permitting Christians and members of other faiths to rest on their weekly holiday."

The phrase "legal day of rest" was left open to interpretation, one of which has been that there should be no public transportation on the Jewish Sabbath. The exception to the rule was Haifa, which had always prided itself on being a mixed city. Grandma has grown frustrated with this exception.

In 2019-2020 several other cities experimented with public transportation on Shabbat. These moves were roundly condemned by ultra-Orthodox leaders in particular, who moved to make sure the law forbade contravening the "status quo" in this way. MK Tamar Zandberg fought for the buses to keep running on Shabbat, so as to help out in particular those who do not own a car. If, Zandberg went on to opine, the government bans public transportation on Shabbat, they should also insist that the government-provided cars given to every minister should also remain unused throughout the sabbath! (Her recommendation was not adopted.)

 # QUESTIONS FOR FURTHER EXPLORATION

• Should a Jewish space operate according to Jewish traditions?

• Is a Jewish state (with 20 percent non-Jewish citizens) a Jewish space?

• Which other countries do things according to their particular culture?

• What particular ways of doing things are upheld in your country?

• Should a country uphold certain ways of doing things based on its particular culture, even if a minority does not want to sustain them?

THOUGHTS TO RETURN TO AFTER A NIGHT'S SLEEP

1   I wish I'd said ...

2   That idea I rejected, now that I think about it ...

3   That whole conversation reminded me of ...

"ARGUMENTS ARE TO BE AVOIDED: they are always vulgar AND OFTEN CONVINCING."

– Oscar Wilde

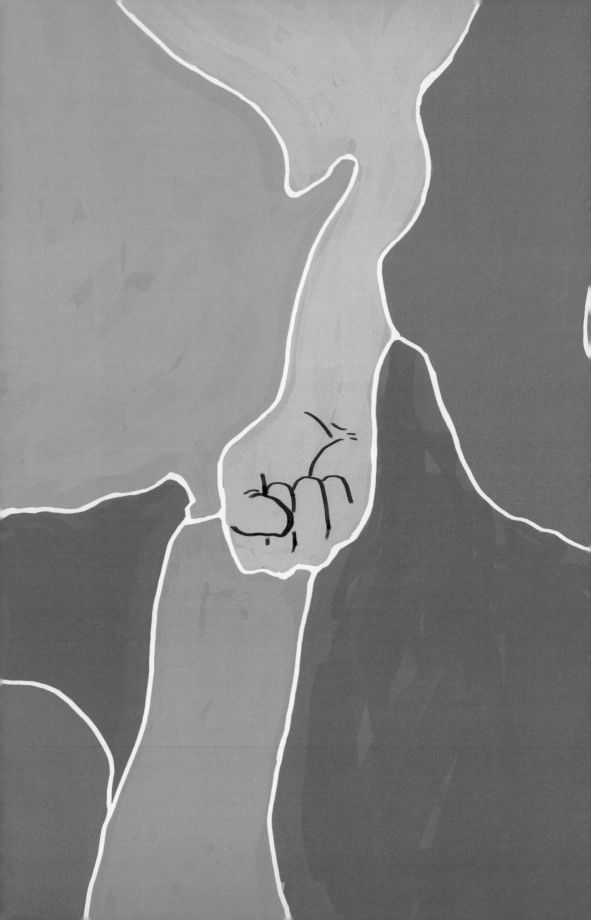

KING OF THE TRAVELERS

A traveler is prevented from entering someone's land. He finds that the owner inherited the land from an ancestor who acquired it through the use of force.

The King of the Travelers was a strong man, with strong arms and a stronger tongue. He would never give way without a fight, and if not a fight, then an argument.

One night he and his people arrived at some nice flat land, and began to set up camp for a while. Suddenly a car drew up, and a flustered man stepped out.

"Oy! You lot! You can't stay here! This is private property!" he shouted.

The King of the Travelers ignored him and waved everyone to carry on unpacking.

"I said, this is private land! You've no right to be here!"

The king's ears pricked up. He turned away from his caravan and calmly said, "I have many rights. Many rights indeed. And seeing as this here is private land, I promise to be right and private while I'm here."

"It's my land! It's my land, and I want you all to leave!"

"Your land is it? And how do you know it's your land?"

The man looked back quizzically, never having been asked this before. "I know it's my land because my father gave it to me."

"And how did your father know it was his?"

"Because his father gave it to him. And his father before him."

"And how did your great-grandfather come to own this land?"

"Because his father gave it to him. And his father before him."

"And how did your great-great-great-grandfather come to own the land?"

"Well, he, er, it was hundreds of years ago," hesitated the landowner.

"Even many hundreds of years ago, how did he come to own the land?"

"He fought someone for it."

"Did he indeed?" said the King of Travelers, smiling, beginning to roll up his sleeves. "So now I'll fight you for it . . . "

GUIDING QUESTIONS

• If the King of Travelers wins the fight, should the land become his?

• Why? Why not?

BACKGROUND

This classic tale (first heard from Rory McLeod) asks a question about force, and about time, in assessing the legitimacy of ownership. It might be that if one goes far enough back in time, one will find that nearly every piece of land was once taken off another by force. Is there a "statute of limitations" on stealing another's land or not?

For example, in the late 1700s, the large city of San Antonio was the capital of Tejas, a province of New Spain (soon to become Mexico). After a series of wars in the mid-1800s, the United States of America took ownership of San Antonio.

Following our story of the King of Travelers, we might wonder what would happen if a Mexican were one day to knock on the door of a house in San Antonio and demand his land back. The current owner in the twenty-first century would no doubt refer not to an ancestor's fight but to a deed of sale. Yet the Mexican incarnation of the King of Travelers would see this as proof of an illegal sale of stolen goods. The land was "stolen" by force. Might the Mexican not be within his rights to use force to take it back?

And if the Mexican were to take back San Antonio land from the American, what next? What if a Payaya Native American were to then arrive, demanding his land back from the stealing Spanish colonial authorities?

Where does it end? Should it ever end?

Should there ever be a point where we might accept the legitimacy of a conquest?

We refer to a Mexican/American example, but the example of Israel is of course even more pertinent. Justified or unjustified, necessary or unnecessary, the State of Israel and its territory was mostly gained through fighting. Although the State of Israel was granted land from the Balfour Declaration (1917) to the United Nations in 1947, who granted it? Was it theirs to grant? The rulers of the land of Israel in the early twentieth century were the British. From which rulers was the land taken? The Ottoman Empire. And who did they take it from? The Mamelukes? And before them Salah ad Din? And before them the Crusaders? And before them the Romans? And the Maccabees? Macedonians? Babylonians? Israelites? Egyptians? And what of the battles that Joshua's forces fought when reclaiming the Promised Land? Or should we look to Isaac and Ishmael?

QUESTIONS FOR FURTHER EXPLORATION

- Where does it end? Should it ever end?

- Should there ever be a point where we might accept the legitimacy of a conquest?

 ## THOUGHTS TO RETURN TO AFTER A NIGHT'S SLEEP

1. I wish I'd said …

2. That idea I rejected, now that I think about it …

3. That whole conversation reminded me of …

SECURITY BARRIER

Nadia's route to school is disrupted by a fence meant to protect someone else. Is it fair?

Nadia woke up with her usual morning energy. After rushing through breakfast, she ran out of the house, excited to continue work on her art project at school. As usual, she skipped through the trees at the back of her house and set off on the short walk across the fields to school.

She stopped. There it was, standing there, some hundred yards away: a huge, brand-new iron fence. As she approached it, Nadia could see that the new fence stretched all around the school and the next-door Nursing Home. Instead of arriving at school in a hop and a skip, it now took her over half an hour to walk all around this barrier to reach the sole entrance at the front. On the way, she also noticed that her friends' favorite spot, by that clump of eucalyptus trees, was outside of the fence, so that at playtime they'd not even be able to hang out there.

By the time Nadia made it inside the school, she was furious. She stormed up to her art teacher, with a belly full of complaints. "Why have they fenced off the school? What about our rights? What about our freedom to walk around? What about our clump of eucalyptus trees?

What, are we in prison now?"

Her teacher looked at Nadia sadly and walked her out to the playground. From there they could see the Nursing Home across the way. Nadia could not help but notice that all the windows were smashed, and the side of the building was covered in graffiti. "Vandals came in and did this over the weekend," said the teacher grimly. "The Home is officially inside the grounds of the school. To protect the Nursing Home, we have to put the fence around the school as well."

"Yes, but," Nadia began to protest, but stopped herself. She wanted to say that it wasn't her fault vandals had attacked the Care Home. She wanted to say she shouldn't be punished for the deeds of others. She wanted to cry at the barrier suddenly placed between her and her school. She wanted to rail against the damage to open lands and the eucalyptus grove.

But she didn't say a thing. Not yet, anyway.

 # GUIDING QUESTIONS

- After thinking, what do you think Nadia should say? To whom?

- What should she do?

- What would you do or say?

BACKGROUND

The story of Nadia is not intended to present a perfect analogy to the Israeli-Palestinian situation. It should by no means be used to map references one-to-one. It is instead intended to help develop a shared language—a more morally varied vocabulary to begin to talk about the specifics of the security barrier/Apartheid Wall.

The Green Line is what divides internationally recognized Israel from the disputed/occupied territories of the West Bank (what Israeli Jews tend to call Judea and Samaria). Over the Green Line, key issues for Palestinians, such as water rights, land rights, and freedom of movement, are in the hands of the Israeli military. Whenever the future borders of a Palestinian state are discussed, key reference is made to the Green Line.

The public pressure for a barrier along the Green Line grew from September 2000 until 2003, as West Bank-based Palestinians carried out seventy-three terror attacks in which 293 Israelis were killed and 1,950 were wounded. Israel's stated motivation for building the barrier was to prevent terror attacks on civilians inside Israel, by Palestinian attackers from the West Bank. As then-Senator Hillary Clinton pointed out at the time, the security barrier was a nonviolent way to prevent terrorism.

Since the start of the barrier's construction began, the number of attacks declined by more than 90 percent. The number of Israelis murdered and wounded decreased by more than 70 percent and 85 percent, respectively, following the erection of the barrier. There were, undoubtedly, many causes for this drop in attacks, but the significance of the barrier cannot be ignored.

Many expected the security barrier to be constructed along the Green Line. In practice, this barrier takes a much more meandering route, cutting into the West Bank/Judea and Samaria. Eighty-five percent of the barrier—sometimes a massive concrete wall, sometimes a fence—actually goes over the Green Line and into territory that is not under Israeli sovereignty. It often runs through Palestinian villages, cuts off farmers from their lands, and even "traps" thirty-two Palestinian villages that are on the Palestinian side of the Green Line, but on the Israeli side of the barrier.

As a result, Palestinians call it the Apartheid Wall, or the Separation Wall, and condemn it as a tool of racial oppression and territorial theft.

 ## QUESTIONS FOR FURTHER EXPLORATION

• Where are there barriers (physical walls or fences) in your life?

• Who decided where the barriers should be put? How did they decide?

• What would you say is good about barriers? What is bad about barriers?

THOUGHTS TO RETURN TO AFTER A NIGHT'S SLEEP

1 I wish I'd said ...

2 That idea I rejected, now that I think about it ...

3 That whole conversation reminded me of ...

"I AM TOTALLY DOWN WITH DISAGREEMENT. I don't like Haterade, BUT DISAGREEMENT IS WONDERFUL."

— ROXANE GAY

TMI

> Should she keep her son away from a friend whose father posts horrible opinions on social media?

My son Dani has been playing with his friend Omer since he was a baby. They were in *maon* (daycare) together. They went to *gan* (preschool) together, and now they are in first grade together.

Omer's parents seem really nice. His mom is lots of fun and is always helping others. I rarely end up speaking much with Omer's dad. He's often outside with the kids in the backyard or in the kitchen whipping up some treats for his children and their friends. He has a certain kind of energy that makes him a kid magnet. He even taught my Dani how to head a soccer ball!

So the kids stay close, and the parents mainly operate as a taxi system, seeing each other briefly at drop-offs and pickups. We're in several WhatsApp groups together. At some point, we became friends on Facebook. The usual parent stuff.

One day, as I'm mindlessly scrolling through Facebook, I see what I consider to be quite a disturbing post. It says, "What kind of jerks believe that?" and it was posted by Omer's dad. I continue scrolling and see more posts by Omer's dad. This one says, "These traitors should all be put up against a wall and shot!" And believe me, the people he wants shot are not, by any stretch of the imagination, "traitors." But they certainly stand for things that Omer's dad doesn't agree with.

And I know I shouldn't go there, but it's the way of social media, isn't it? I can't stop myself. I click on to his Facebook page. It's full of so much rage, so much barely concealed desire for violence. So much intolerance.

The next day, Omer's mom calls to invite Dani over to play. I hesitate.

Should I discuss Omer's dad's posts with him? Online or in person?

Should I let my son play in the house of someone who espouses such extreme views, and in such unkind ways?

Or should I just unfriend Omer's dad on Facebook and stay ignorant of the views of a man who is often responsible for my son?

GUIDING QUESTIONS

• What should she do? Why?

BACKGROUND

The tale is told of the great Rabbi Elisha ben Abuya, living at the turn of the second century. He was a great mind, a brilliant teacher, who was deemed to have contravened the most basic understandings of morality in that time. He was shunned and excluded from all society. Only one student, the independent-minded Rabbi Meir, would still go to study with Rabbi Elisha, despite the fact that he was officially excommunicated.

When questioned as to his insistence on learning from this disgraced man, Rabbi Meir was said to have answered that one can eat the fruit of a pomegranate while throwing away its peel. The implication: one can benefit from a person even if they are not perfect, by partaking only of their positive qualities and ignoring or rejecting their flaws.

The mother in TMI is unconvinced that her son will have the discernment to filter his friend's father in such a way.

QUESTIONS FOR FURTHER EXPLORATION

- In these days of social media, do we perhaps simply know too much about people? Are we better off knowing less?

- Much is written about how we might learn to expose less about ourselves online, but is there perhaps also value in investigating less about others? Or should one always make use of information readily available?

 # THOUGHTS TO RETURN TO AFTER A NIGHT'S SLEEP

1   I wish I'd said ...

2   That idea I rejected, now that I think about it ...

3   That whole conversation reminded me of ...

"I'm sorry to say that THE SUBJECT I MOST DISLIKED WAS MATHEMATICS. I have thought about it. I THINK THE REASON WAS THAT MATHEMATICS LEAVES NO ROOM FOR ARGUMENT. IF YOU MADE A MISTAKE, THAT WAS ALL THERE WAS TO IT."

– MALCOLM X –

WHY THE HECK SHOULD I VOTE?

> Palestinian residents of East Jerusalem are not allowed to
> participate in Israel's general elections, but they are allowed to vote
> in Jerusalem's municipal elections. The vast majority do not vote,
> choosing to reject the legitimacy of the regime. A Palestinian woman
> has second thoughts.

Why the heck should I vote? In their elections? Crazy.

You know they don't let me vote in their national elections, right? They let
me vote in the local elections—big whoop. Why should I care about voting
for the mayor of Jerusalem if I can't vote for the prime minister of the whole
country?

I'm a Palestinian. Born in Al Quds—Jerusalem to you—in the house my great-
great-grandfather built. Many, many years before the Jews came and told
me it was their homeland, not mine. Years before they gave Hebrew names
to neighborhoods in Jerusalem that already had names. Years before they
came waving "democracy" as an excuse for taking over my land, my country,
my city.

And now you expect me to vote? It would be like someone invading my house
and giving me a choice about what kind of milk to put in the fridge. I don't
care about the milk—get out of my house!

Look, between us, that analogy doesn't completely work. Of course I would care about what milk to put in the fridge. I'm lactose-intolerant.

Same with voting in the Jerusalem elections. However much I hate this system, it would be great to have a say on how my city should be run. If all of us Palestinians chose to vote in the local elections, we'd be able to get them to fix our terrible roads, and finally clear the garbage. Maybe they'd stop demolishing our houses when we build them after they don't give us permits.

I work in schools as an educational psychologist. There are 370 of us in all of Jerusalem, but only thirty-seven in all of the Palestinian side of the city. I'm rushed off my feet and never feel like I've given my clients enough time or attention. If we all voted, we could change that. Right now I'm paying all my taxes to them but not getting to tell them what to do with the money. It's crazy.

But then if I vote, I'm telling them that their system is fine. If I voted I'd be telling them that I'm not a Palestinian anymore. I'd be giving up who I am. Who we are. What they are.

I don't know what to do . . .

Printed with kind permission of Ir Amim

Greater Jerusalem 2021

GUIDING QUESTIONS

• What should she do?

BACKGROUND

In 1967, in the Six-Day War that Israel fought against Jordan, Syria, and Egypt, Israel conquered land, including that which is today called East Jerusalem. This war is perhaps most famous for the Israeli recapturing of the Temple Mount, including the Western Wall. As a result of this war, Israel redrew its borders, which included taking control of East Jerusalem (all the areas to the right of the green dotted line in the above map.)

The Palestinian people who lived in East Jerusalem at that time were given permanent residency status in Israel. That is, they were not granted citizenship in Israel, but they—and their children and grandchildren—were given all the rights, responsibilities, and services of Israeli citizens, except for two: they were not required to serve in the Israeli army and they could not vote in the general elections. They were, however, permitted to vote in the municipal Jerusalem elections.

The lives of these some 330,000 residents have been impacted greatly by the local political and practical situation of the city in which they live. They are required to pay taxes, and they receive municipal services, including education, water, health, etc. Critics of Israeli policy point to the poor living conditions in much of East Jerusalem, saying that the Jerusalem municipality is not living up to its end of the bargain, as it does not provide equal services to East Jerusalem residents.

In 2018, FP (foreignpolicy.com) reported as follows:
"Jihan, 39, who works for a Palestinian human rights organization and spoke on the condition that her name be changed to protect her anonymity, told FP that the 'Palestinian Authority has always said that we should forgo the struggle for a better standard of living and our civil rights, because it would mean legitimizing the Israeli occupation.'"

But, she argued, "The Palestinian Authority hasn't done anything for us, either. They use Jerusalem as a symbol to maintain their position in the Arab world as the defenders of the holy city. But they don't care about us, the real people who live here and love this city." She was so fed up that she decided to vote in the municipal elections.

"East Jerusalemites are schizophrenic," Jihan explained. "Palestinians on the West Bank resent us because we have benefits and options that they don't have. Palestinians who live in Israel and have full citizenship think of us as West Bankers. And we're certainly not Israelis. Voting could be a way forward, because we Jerusalemites have to fend for ourselves."

In 2013, Daniel Seidemann, the director of Terrestrial Jerusalem, reported that less than 1 percent of eligible Palestinian residents of East Jerusalem voted, and in 2018 the number was lower than 3 percent. Recently, a few Palestinian East Jerusalem residents took another step, and decided to run for city council and even for mayor. However, after pressure against them and even violence from Palestinians who oppose their participation in normalizing Israeli control, these candidates dropped out of the race.

Questions for Further Exploration

- Are you the kind of person to fight from within a system, or do you choose to fight it from without?

- Would you say that someone's inclination to fight a system depends on external circumstances, or their personality?

 ## Thoughts to Return to After a Night's Sleep

1. I wish I'd said ...

2. That idea I rejected, now that I think about it ...

3. That whole conversation reminded me of ...

"LET US ARGUE OVER
FUNDAMENTALS.
Over things less
than fundamental,
OTHERS HAVE already
ARGUED BEFORE US."

— GALIA EVEN-CHEN

"IT DOES TAKE GREAT MATURITY to understand THAT THE OPINION WE ARE ARGUING FOR IS MERELY THE HYPOTHESIS WE FAVOR, necessarily imperfect, probably transitory, WHICH ONLY VERY LIMITED MINDS CAN DECLARE TO BE A CERTAINTY OR A TRUTH."

– MILAN KUNDERA

Praying at the Kotel

ISRAEL

> A devout woman finds herself tortured by women who come to pray
> at the Kotel in nontraditional ways.

Ever since I was a little girl, every day I would wake up early and walk with
my father and my siblings through the narrow, cobbled streets of the Jewish
quarter of the Old City, down the long flight of stairs, to the Kotel. I adored
that precious moment when my sisters and I would part from my father and
my brothers, and we would make our way to our special place at the sacred
wall. Touching those stones, in our intimate space, made me feel like I was
touching heaven.

I am now fully grown and married, and now my visits to the Kotel are tinged
with sadness. Every morning I lean my forehead on the wall and pray with
all my heart that the Lord may open my womb. Yankel and I have been
married for three years now, but we have not yet been blessed with a baby.
Sometimes I find myself weeping as I touch the cold, sacred stones. I am
comforted by their touch.

The most powerful day for me is Rosh Chodesh. At the new moon is when I
feel my prayers for fertility find their place in the Jewish calendar and in the
heart of the King of the Universe, blessed be He. This is when I feel the gates
of heaven may open for me and my husband.

But recently my pleadings have been disturbed. Every Rosh Chodesh a large group of women, mostly tourists, push their way into our quiet space by the Kotel and sing out loud, dance, and wear shawls as if they were *tallitot* (prayer shawls). Every month, on the exact day that is most important for my prayers for fertility, these people bring their loud political gestures into the deepest synagogue in the world.

Yankel is beside himself with rage. "Who are these people? How dare they trample on the traditions of a place they visit twelve days a year, when my father, my grandfather, and my great-grandfather have prayed here every day? When you, my wife, are praying for our first child?"

He plans to join the protesters next month. Many people in our community are furious with these tourists. They scream, they blow on whistles, and often throw things. They are sometimes violent.

I can't bear the women with their singing. But I also can't bear the behavior of the protesters. Both destroy the sanctity of this place so deeply connected to the Temple home of our Lord. I want to tell Yankel to stay home. But at the same time I sometimes wish I could join him and fight this invasion. If we don't shout and protest, who will stop them?

GUIDING QUESTIONS

- Do you think she should tell Yankel to stay home or encourage him?

- Should she ask the Women of the Wall to give her more respect?

- Have you ever found yourself in a position where your most sacred moments are spoiled by another?

BACKGROUND

The Kotel is often known as the Western Wall. This wall is understood to be the last remnant of the destroyed Second Temple area, which was central to Jewish life some two thousand years ago. Throughout the centuries of Muslim and Christian rule, Jews would gather to pray at the Kotel and mourn the Temple's destruction.

Although it is only the remnants of an outer wall of the Temple area, for centuries it has been regarded as sacred to the Jewish People—the closest a human may approach to the Holy of Holies where divine fire lapped up sacrifices of our High Priest. The Kotel even became known as the "Wailing Wall," because Jews would weep there, mourning the loss of the Temple.

Jewish access to the Kotel has not been easy. Under British rule, Jews were not allowed to blow the shofar at the Kotel on Yom Kippur. From 1948 to 1967, Jordan did not even allow Jews to approach the Kotel at all. It was not until Israel's victory in the Six-Day War of 1967 that Jews were given full access to the Kotel, and almost immediately the Israeli government granted its full control to the chief rabbinate.

The chief rabbinate is the religiously Orthodox state authority over Jewish religious life. From 1967 onward the rabbinate has administered the Kotel according to the traditions of an Orthodox synagogue. "That place certainly can be no less than a synagogue, which is a small Temple. Likewise with regard to the *Halakhot* [religious law] of a synagogue . . . certainly everything that is customary there should apply to the Western Kotel." (former Chief Rabbi Ovadiah Yosef) Since a mechitzah—a partition separating men and women—is customary in an Orthodox synagogue, so a *mechitzah* was erected at the Kotel in the Summer of 1967. It was placed such that the men's area is four times the size of the women's area.

From 1988 onward, women's groups from Israel and around the world have been struggling for the right to pray at the Kotel according to their own more progressive religious traditions. Some demands have been for the right to wear a tallit and to read from a Torah scroll, some for there to be a more equitable distribution of space along the wall between men and women, and recently most initiatives have centered around the development of an area called Robinson's Arch farther along the original wall for mixed progressive prayer. None of these negotiations have succeeded in quieting the basic demands for denominational and gendered equality.

As a result, Women of the Wall convene for women's prayer at the women's section of the Kotel at every new moon. They wear *tallitot*, prayer shawls, "smuggle" a Torah scroll into the women's section, and sing celebratory prayers. This infuriates those Orthodox and ultra-Orthodox Jews who pray at the Kotel every day, who view this kind of behavior as provocative, insensitive, and insulting. As far as they are concerned, these progressives have invaded an orthodox synagogue and are enforcing their foreign traditions through coercion. Reactions are often violent, noisy, and overseen by an ambivalent police force.

QUESTIONS FOR FURTHER EXPLORATION

• Does the violent reaction of the ultra-Orthodox invalidate their protest?

• If one visits and uses a public site daily, does this grant them more rights over the customs of the place than someone who visits once a month?

• Are human-asserted rights more important than God-given faith?

 # THOUGHTS TO RETURN TO AFTER A NIGHT'S SLEEP

1 I wish I'd said …

2 That idea I rejected, now that I think about it …

3 That whole conversation reminded me of …

"Confronting one another across differences means that we must change ideas about how we learn; rather than fearing conflict, we have to find ways to use it as a catalyst for new thinking, for growth."

– bell hooks –

CAT LADY

> On a tiny Israeli Moshav (a village cooperative) a sad and lonely woman loves cats too much for the rest of the Moshav members.

I love our Moshav. It's a beautiful place surrounded by rolling hills and a view of the Kinneret (Sea of Galilee). It's kind of farm land, but we live in proper houses and everything. It's a place where we can run around, visit our friends without booking a playdate, and walk our dogs without our parents worrying. And like every close-knit community, we have our characters. Like the Cat Lady.

I love the Cat Lady. I mean, I don't really talk to her much, but I really love her. They say that she used to have twin boys whom everyone adored, but one died in the war, and the other moved to California. No one ever knew her husband. They say that when her second son left the country, she didn't come out of her house for five years. *Five years.* And ever since then she's always looked sad, like she was going to burst into tears any minute.

Except when she's near a cat.

Whenever she sees a cat, she just becomes a different person. Honestly. I've seen it. This big, gentle smile begins to spread across her face. From a painful hobble she starts to trip along like a little girl, and I swear it's like her wrinkles get this invisible ironing and she looks about fifty years younger!

Any stray cat—she'll immediately feed it and stroke it and dance around with it like it's a newborn baby.

The thing is that stray cats aren't babies, but they do have babies. Lots of them. Right now I can look out of my window at Cat Lady's house, and there must be at least fifty cats hanging around there, waiting for her to come out. There are always cardboard boxes around her place full of adorable, cuddly kittens. When they're kittens they're always so cute.

Ada next door complained that all the cats were making a mess in her garden. The Cohens down the road said the cats had gotten into their porch and used their furniture as a claw sharpener. The stoop outside the Makolet corner shop always smells like cat pee no matter how many times Yossi cleans it. And all the children of the Moshav refuse to throw out the trash anymore, because whenever they do, a cat suddenly jumps out of the dumpster and frightens them to death.

I wasn't a great fan, either. Just the other day I found a cat outside playing with my favorite doll! And when I tried to take her back, the cat suddenly hissed at me and tried to scratch me!

Last night Mom and Dad came home from a Moshav meeting. They decided they were going to vote on a new bylaw that says no one in the Moshav would be allowed more than two cats per household. They said that Cat Lady just sat there throughout the meeting, looking really sad.

I can just imagine her walking home, with that cat-less, lonely limp. It made me sad. But then, when I'm sad I normally hug my doll, and I couldn't do that because that cat had taken it . . .

GUIDING QUESTIONS

- How would you vote in the Moshav meeting?

- Why?

BACKGROUND

While this story is fictional, the cat problem in Israel is real. In the 1930s, under the British Mandate, cats were brought to Israel to deal with the rat infestation that was plaguing Israel at the time. And ever since then, the cats have reproduced. Today, it is estimated that there are about two million street cats around the country. Public policy and public health experts continually struggle with questions of how to deal with this issue.

In our story, in addition to the public hazard that the cats create, we have a woman who needs to be cared for as well, and cats that ought to be treated humanely.

Jewish texts shed some light on these competing values:

Compassion for those in need: In the Talmud (*Masechet Sotah*) we are asked to walk in God's ways. In the same way that God is compassionate, so too, we need to be compassionate. Cat Lady certainly needs compassion. Compassion is so important that it is considered a Godly attribute. The fact that the narrator doesn't even use the name of the main character is a sign that at least some level of compassion is missing.

Treatment of animals: Jewish tradition also tells us to treat animals well. The Torah lists many ways in which we must care for animals. In Exodus 20:10 animals are almost likened to humans, in that it is written that animals, like people, must be given a day of rest on Shabbat. In the Talmud (*Baba Metzia* 32b), we learn that we must relieve an animal's burden if it's too much for it.

Keeping our neighborhoods clean: In addition to ancient Jewish sources (such as the Talmud) telling us the importance of keeping our neighborhoods clean, more modern sources do as well. In 1860, the first neighborhood to be built outside of Jerusalem's Old City walls, Mishkenot Sha'ananim, was established, and rules for cleanliness were set as well. The bylaws for this then very poor neighborhood, stated: "Every inhabitant of the Mishkenot Sha'ananim neighborhood shall command his charges to purge his house on a daily basis of all garbage and any unclean matter; he shall also sprinkle clean water on the floor of the rooms of his house at least once a day." And, "Every inhabitant of the Mishkenot Sha'ananim neighborhood shall command his charges not to cast away any garbage in front of his house, and shall clean up all the areas around his dwelling, and throw away the garbage in the designated area and cover it immediately."

QUESTIONS FOR FURTHER EXPLORATION

- Are human beings more important than animals such as cats?

- If you feed a stray cat, does that make you responsible for everything it does?

- To what extent should a community be able to make decisions for its members? What communities/groups/organizations have you been a part of that have made choices for their members? How did this make you feel?

THOUGHTS TO RETURN TO AFTER A NIGHT'S SLEEP

1 I wish I'd said ...

2 That idea I rejected, now that I think about it ...

3 That whole conversation reminded me of ...

"NOTHING FIRMS UP
A FRIENDSHIP like
a good-natured
ARGUMENT."

- Lemony Snicket

SHE'S NOT A REFUGEE!

> Her sister's cleaner is an illegal immigrant. Should she report her?
> Even if it also affects the cleaner's innocent children?

I've got a problem with my sister's cleaner.

Don't get me wrong, Maria's a lovely woman, and a great cleaner, as far my sister's concerned. But she's illegal. And I'm in law enforcement.

She came to Israel on a work visa. She agreed to its conditions. She signed, committing to stay in Israel for five years.

She lied. After the five years were up, she didn't go home as she'd promised. She went rogue. She stayed on, illegally, for another fifteen years. She worked illegally, not paying taxes and not keeping her end of the bargain with the state. She didn't run away from the Philippines in fear for her life, and it's not dangerous for her to return. She's not a refugee. She's not.

I should turn her in. My sister would never find out who did it.

The problem is that during this time she's had two kids. Nice kids. Both of them born here. Great Hebrew, work hard at school. Never even visited the Philippines in their lives. What would happen with them?

It's not the Americas here. In Israel, as in the rest of the world, you don't automatically become a citizen just because you were born here. Just like their mother, they're not citizens of Israel, and they're here illegally.

If I turn her in, her kids will have to go with her. Israel wouldn't separate the kids from their mom. The whole family would be kicked out, and these kids with an Israeli education and Israeli friends would be forced to live in what is, for all intents and purposes, a foreign country.

But if I let her be, I'm rewarding a cheat. If I saw a shoplifter, I wouldn't keep quiet, even if it was a single mother with kids. What's the difference? And all the while, real refugees who really fled here in fear for their lives, who really can't go home, they're the ones getting a bad rap. It's not fair. Real refugees are the ones who need our support, not cheap labor who lie.

 GUIDING QUESTIONS

- Should she report her?

- What, if any, difference is there between reporting a shoplifter and reporting an illegal migrant worker?

BACKGROUND

In many countries, Israel included, lower-income, less desirable jobs are often filled by migrants. In 2021, there were about 324,000 migrant workers employed in Israel. According to the Knesset Research and Information Center, 37 percent of these workers are in the country illegally. As in our story, some number of migrants enter the country on a legal work visa but then stay in the country after the visa has expired.

Many of these migrants come to Israel in their twenties or thirties, with the hope of earning a better income than in their home countries and often send funds back home to help their families. Not infrequently, over the course of the standard five-year visa, these folks get married, have children, and establish roots in Israel.

These children, as in our story, do not automatically become citizens (being born in Israel does not confer citizenship). But they do take on the Israeli culture. They study in Israeli schools, learn the language, eat the food. When it comes time for their parents to leave, while legally they are bound to leave, emotionally it is a lot to ask a parent to pick up his or her family and move back to a place they no longer call home. In the words of Beth Franco, a worker from the Philippines and an advocate with United Children of Israel, "After twenty-one years serving the Jews and Israelis, especially the elderly, I think they can be compassionate to our children and let them live their dreams and have a better future. It's better here for our children. They don't have Jewish blood, but in every sense of the word they are Israelis."

There are Israelis, including important policymakers who offer a different perspective on economic grounds. According to 2020 research by the Knesset's Research and Information Center on the economic effects of illegal immigration, Israel spent about half a billion shekels on issues related to migrant workers. The research explains that these workers effectively take money out of the country and diminish the employment opportunities for Israelis. In 2009, the Finance Minister Yuval Steinitz was quoted as saying, "What's going on is an outrage. There are 100,000 people taking jobs illegally while Israelis remain unemployed. The plan must involve painful economic sanctions on those who employ illegal workers."

 ## QUESTIONS FOR FURTHER EXPLORATION

- What, if anything, is wrong with giving immediate citizenship to anyone who lives and works in your country?

- Why do you think most countries do not give automatic citizenship to babies born in their territory?

- In what way should Israel respond differently to migrant workers than other countries?

THOUGHTS TO RETURN TO AFTER A NIGHT'S SLEEP

1. I wish I'd said …

2. That idea I rejected, now that I think about it …

3. That whole conversation reminded me of …

"THE difficult conversation WILL STRENGTHEN TRUST."

– Esther Perel

RACIAL PROFILING

> A security guard finds himself using a racial profiling that might equally be applied against him.

What am I supposed to do? Tell me, what am I supposed to do?

It's a job. I need the job. I have debts. Don't we all? It's a job. A terrifying job. I do security at the mall. Everyone who comes into the mall, I have to check them. Check they don't have a bomb on them. Great. Because if they do, they're sure to just hand it over to me, right? No, not right. Terrifying. But it's a job.

So where are they all coming from, these suicide bombers? Are they Israelis, or are they Palestinians? Are they Jewish or are they Muslim? Last I checked, crazy people coming into this mall with suicide vests—only Palestinian Muslims. I know the equation, you don't have to tell me. Not every Palestinian Muslim is a suicide bomber, of course not. But every suicide bomber in this part of the world is a Palestinian Muslim.

So when a guy comes along, and he's got darker skin than everyone else, and he's unshaven, and he's got cheap-looking clothes, and he looks kind of nervous - you telling me I should treat him like everyone else? You telling me I shouldn't take him aside, safely away from the rest of the line, and search him straight away? You telling me I should be totally calm when I might be checking the guy who's about to blow me up? Right.

So I'm nervous and he's nervous. And neither of us has shaved recently. And we're the same color skin more or less—proud Yemenite stock, me! And for a second, just a second, I know that if I were to see me coming up to the line, I'd take me aside to search just like I'm searching him.

I look him in the eye, and he looks me in the eye, and something inside me wants to just let him walk through without extra screening.

GUIDING QUESTIONS

• Should he let him through without a full screening?

• Should this form of "racial profiling" stop?

BACKGROUND

This is a story that emerges from the early 2000s in Israel. During the four-year period that came to be known in Israel as the Second Intifada, the country was flooded with Palestinian suicide bombers.

At an average of nearly three suicide bombings every month, some 127 bombings took place between 2001 and 2004, killing 566 people and wounding 706. All suicide bombings were carried out by Palestinians. We know this not only because the perpetrators were often found on camera footage, but also because their respective organizations claimed credit for the attacks.

During this time, entrance to all public transportation, restaurants, and public buildings was subject to security checks. Sometimes checks were thorough—emptying bags, frisking—and sometimes one would be asked a question or two and waved through.

Officially or unofficially, racial profiling was employed. Indeed, *not* to assume that an Arab-looking young man was a greater risk than a Jewish-looking woman was almost seen as foolish. Israeli airport security prides itself on enabling shorter lines and provably achieving much greater safety on flights, thanks to its unashamed use of racial profiling.

This approach, what some label racist and what others label common sense, has not only challenged the rights and identity of Palestinians. It can also affect the lives of Israeli Jews whose origins are from Arab lands. Mizrachi Jewish Israelis, originating from North Africa or Syria or Yemen, can often look similar to the people security guards are watching out for. There have been numerous instances where a Mizrachi Israeli Jew has either been wrongfully detained or even wrongfully attacked on suspicion of being a Palestinian suicide bomber.

In this story, the narrator is himself of Yemenite origin and can imagine himself falling prey to the racial profiling he himself is employing.

QUESTIONS FOR FURTHER EXPLORATION

- (When) should our safety be compromised for the sake of equity?

- (When) should equity be compromised for the sake of safety?

- Is there a human right to safety? And if so, does it have limitations?

 # THOUGHTS TO RETURN TO AFTER A NIGHT'S SLEEP

1 I wish I'd said …

2 That idea I rejected, now that I think about it …

3 That whole conversation reminded me of …

"LET'S INVITE ONE ANOTHER IN. MAYBE THEN WE CAN BEGIN TO FEAR LESS, to make fewer wrong assumptions, TO LET GO OF THE BIASES AND STEREOTYPES THAT unnecessarily DIVIDE US."

- Michelle Obama

"A MATURE SOCIETY UNDERSTANDS that at the heart of democracy IS ARGUMENT."

— SALMAN RUSHDIE

GIVE ME RESPECT!

> A religious taxi driver will not/cannot shake the hand of a customer at the end of the ride, because she is a woman. She does not accept this behavior.

Oh, this is great. Now I'm going to get a bad review. Now they're going to reduce my rating. That's really going to mess up my daily income.

So unfair.

We had a really nice conversation. Talking about this, talking about that. Me giving her my opinion—it's what I call cab driver generosity—happy to keep giving! And she's, shall we say, being generous right back! It was a long trip, with a good amount of traffic as we came into the city, and together we pretty much put the world to rights. She was a fun fare.

When we reached her destination she took care to register a generous tip in her app, but then she does it.

She reaches out to touch my hand. Like she wants to shake my hand. Like we're equals, like we're friends, like we're sharing the same world and she wants to give me respect. I smile at her real nice, hold my hands together without taking hers, and give her a little bow of my head.

She smiles back but doesn't take her hand away. She pushes it toward my hand. I can't touch her. She must know I can't touch her. We've been talking about religion and politics the whole journey. She can see how I'm dressed. She must know that my religion won't allow me to touch a woman who's not my wife. But her hand is still there. I hold my hands up in a kind of cross between "I surrender" and "No farther, please," and wish her well in all her future endeavors.

She looks annoyed.

"Why won't you shake my hand?"

And it's not really a question, it's more of a demand.

I smile awkwardly, and shrug. "I can't. My religion. You know."

She shrugs, but not so nicely. "If I were a man, you'd shake my hand."

"Well, it's a bit more complicated than—"

"So disrespectful!" She cuts in. "Why can you give respect to men but not to women?"

I should have kept my mouth shut. I should have slowed down, I know. But by the time I reached for my mouth brakes, it had already screeched out: "Why do you give respect to women but not to the religious?"

And that was it. She blew up, I blew up back, and here I am with zero stars on the ride app and a bad review.

I know I should have kept my mouth brakes on, but still. She should never have tried to force me to shake hands. Right?

GUIDING QUESTIONS

- Should she have "tried to force" him to shake hands?

- Should he have agreed to do so?

CONTEXT

A famous tale is told in Israeli circles of an impasse in 1952 between then Prime Minister David Ben-Gurion and the respected leader of the orthodox community, known as the Chazon Ish. Ben-Gurion asked the Chazon Ish how he expected the secular and the religious in Israel to avoid inevitable clashes in the way the country should be run.

The Chazon Ish referred to a classic Talmudic parable of an impasse between two camels trying to walk along a narrow path, with no room for both of them. One camel must give way and allow the other to walk ahead. According to tradition, the camel with no load on its back must give way to the camel with the full load on its back.

The point the Chazon Ish was making was that the religious are like a camel loaded up with many of the Lord's commandments to fulfill, while the modern secular "camel" is free of such obligations. Therefore, suggested the Chazon Ish, when at an impasse, modern secular people should always give way to the traditional religious. (In later years this anecdote tended to be told about an empty and a full wagon.)

Some secular Israelis have found themselves caught in a paradox of their own making vis-à-vis this parable. Some will argue that their "camel" or "wagon" is not empty at all. It is also full of many values and principles. One of these principles is of equality, for example. However, another one of these "modern secular" principles is tolerance of others, which might lead them to accept the demands of the religious even while rejecting their basis.

Some other modern secularists will argue that they cannot tolerate the denigration of women, irrespective of traditional religious sensibilities. On this issue they cannot and will not give way. This perspective argues that "religion" has been behind too many examples of discrimination against women throughout history for it to be a sufficient defense for treating women differently today.

Of course in our story, the driver in "Give Me Respect" may be of any faith in any country. He could be Muslim, he could be Jewish. But the narrow path is still there. Whose principles are "emptier," less worthy of respect? Whose load is full?

QUESTIONS FOR FURTHER EXPLORATION

"A man's religious faith should always be valued higher than society-formed customs."

• What do you think of this statement? Why?

 ## THOUGHTS TO RETURN TO AFTER A NIGHT'S SLEEP

1 I wish I'd said ...

2 That idea I rejected, now that I think about it ...

3 That whole conversation reminded me of ...

"WE ALL LOSE WHEN BULLYING AND PERSONAL ATTACKS BECOME A SUBSTITUTE for genuine conversation AND PRINCIPLED DISAGREEMENT."

— ALICIA GARZA

Reformim and Kibbush

A regular family argument about Israeli politics reveals that Mom must give up on one crucial issue in order to solve another.

Mom and Uncle Yitzhok were arguing again. Normally they would start after the soup, but this time they were already at it before *kiddush*. Mom and her brother were really close and really different. She lived in Ramat Gan, with me and our dog. He lived in Bnei Brak with his wife and his seven kids, my cousins. Once a month we'd walk over to their place for Friday night, so that Mom could shout at her brother about politics, and he could shout back, and that way they'd know they still loved each other. Or at least that's how Mom always explained it.

This time Mom was on about the *kibbush*, the occupation of the Palestinians, and how we needed to let them have their own state, and Uncle Yitzhok kept annoying her.

"I don't care!" he kept yelling. "I don't care what happens to the *goyim*! I only care about what happens to *Am Yisroel*!"

Mom was already a little flushed from the walk, but Yitzhok's use of the word "goyim" (non-Jews) and "Am Yisroel" (People of Israel) turned her bright red. "How can you say you don't care! These are human beings we're talking about!" Yitzhok shrugged with an annoying smile, probably the same annoying smile he'd been annoying his little sister with for decades.

"Hang on a minute," said Mom, trying a new tactic. "If you don't care what happens with the Palestinians, then why not support us trying to end the kibbush? If you don't care either way, why do you *Haredim* always side with the right-wingers?"

"Because of the *Reformim*!" cried Yitzhok, referring to Reform Jews. "If you lefties stopped letting the Reformim pretend they're Jewish, and stopped allowing women to be rabbis, G-d forbid, we'll let you do what you want with the Palestinians."

Mom was silent for a second. Room for me to say something, because I was starving . . .

"Mom, that sounds like a good deal, doesn't it? You always tell me I need to learn to compromise. Can't you compromise? Forget the Reformim and save the Palestinians. How about it?"

But Mom was already shaking her head. "It's not that simple . . ."

GUIDING QUESTIONS

- Is Mom wrong to reject this compromise?

- What might she say next?

BACKGROUND

This is far from being a fictional issue in Israel. Moshe Gafni, Haredi member of the Knesset and leader of the Degel HaTorah faction has pretty much laid out the same argument Yitzhok used in the story.

In a 2017 interview with left-wing news outlet *Ha'aretz*, he explained that the Haredi distance from the Left is due to their openness to progressive Judaism: "It's because you sit with the Reform Jews. We don't recognize them at all, they hurt the Jewish people. The Reform Jews for me are the most serious problem." He went on to say that were the Left to stand with the Haredim against pluralism in Israel, the Haredim might stand with the Left on issues regarding the Palestinians.

In Israel, "Left" and "Right" tend to be defined more narrowly than in other countries. In Israel, "Left" and "Right" are almost exclusively designated according to one's attitude to the establishment of a Palestinian state alongside Israel. The more willing one is to risk Israeli security in order for a Palestinian state to be established, the more "Left" one is. If one is unwilling or mostly unwilling to take a risk in the establishment of a Palestinian state, one is on the Right.

The Far Left might be expected to ignore security concerns and even argue that the establishment of a Palestinian state would make Israel safer. The Far Right would reject any and every move to establish a Palestinian state.

MK Gafni was signaling that his party, which often holds the balance of power in Israeli elections, does not necessarily take a stand on the issue of the Palestinians. This is not at the heart of their concerns. And so their support is given to whoever supports what is important to the Haredi community, whether they be Left or Right.

The argument goes that all the Left would need to do, in order to build a government that clears the way for a Palestinian state, would be to side with the Haredim against pluralism.

Whether Gafni should be taken at his word, whether one enormous compromise on the Left would immediately lead to a seismic shift in Israeli politics is moot. What is clear, though, is that even the hypothetical question is currently being rejected out of hand. The child in the story is daring to ask it: "Forget the Reformim and save the Palestinians. How about it?"

QUESTIONS FOR FURTHER EXPLORATION

- Some compromises are painful yet crucial because they lead to a valuable outcome. But some compromises must be rejected because they are so painful they undermine or corrupt the values that underlie the reasons for the compromise. How do we tell the difference?

- When is a compromise "the fly in the ointment," and when is it "a cockroach in the soup?" "The best soup is totally spoiled by even one cockroach," teaches Israeli philosopher Avishai Margalit. "Ideals may tell us something important about who we would like to be, but compromises tell us who we are."

 ## THOUGHTS TO RETURN TO AFTER A NIGHT'S SLEEP

1. I wish I'd said …

2. That idea I rejected, now that I think about it …

3. That whole conversation reminded me of …

The Demands of History

Can she give up the farm that holds such sentimental value, for the sake of her son's welfare?

ALLEGORY

I was sitting outside on my back *mirpeset* (porch) with my husband of thirty-five years. We were each deep in thought about how we could help our son Elad.

Elad has fallen on hard times. It's a long story, but basically, through no fault of his own, he has lost all he has. And he's incredible. Truly. A guy with a PhD, speaks three languages, and is kind. He just needs some money to get him back on his feet.

You see, we don't come from a rich family. But we do have a piece of land. A piece of land that could be sold.

Our house overlooks the rolling hills of the Golan. In the winter, it's green and lush. In the summer, it's filled with tourists seeking a getaway from the bigger cities, including my grandchildren. The land that my house is built on—nearly two acres—was handed down to me from my great-great-great-grandfather.

There's a beautiful grove of trees at the end of the property, all trees planted by my family. My great-grandfather started a tradition. Every time a baby was born in our family, a tree was planted. My great-grandfather planted three trees, my father planted four trees, and I planted another two trees.

It became such a sacred site for me that my husband and I were married there. And, in fact, both my great-grandfather and grandfather are buried on the far edge of our property. I, too, plan to be buried here one day.

"We need to sell an acre of our land," my husband said to me after a long silence. "Elad needs the money. Think of what a real difference in Elad's life it would make."

"We can't sell the land. It has so much history. Our family's story is literally planted here," I replied.

"I know. And it would be hard to sell. But isn't the future of our son and grandchildren more important than our history?"

"How can you say such a thing?" I fumed. "Selling my history is like giving away who I am."

"Really? When Israel wanted to include Rachel's tomb on the Palestinian side of the border, we were both in favor of handing it over to help create peace," my husband gently reminded me.

"Yeah, but that was different," I said.

GUIDING QUESTIONS

- Should the couple sell their piece of land?

- What sacred places or special objects (an inherited necklace, perhaps) would you be willing to give up to help a loved one?

- What would you not be willing to give up? Why?

BACKGROUND

Once you've spent time reading and discussing this story, we recommend introducing the allegorical understanding of this story as well. This story explores the question of whether Israel ought to give up land to Palestinians in order to create a thriving future. Roughly speaking, selling the family land can be read as comparable to Israel giving land to the Palestinian Authority in exchange for peace.

The wife in our story represents the importance of the emotional, historical, and even holy attachments that a People has to a place. In the modern-day challenge of drawing borders and boundaries and creating peace agreements, the husband represents those who would side with those who want to give land to the Palestinians to help achieve peace and justice.

This allegory plays out particularly clearly in the modern conflict over Rachel's Tomb, the sacred place where the Jewish matriarch Rachel is buried, as the biblical story explains. Rachel is an important symbol of hope. Rachel's Tomb, for many, is the place where women go to pray for fertility. She is the biblical figure who cries for her children to return safely from war, invoked in Jeremiah 31:15: "A voice was heard in Ramah, lamentation, and bitter weeping; Rachel weeping for her children, refused to be comforted for her children . . . "

In Jewish tradition, Rachel's Tomb is seen in the same way as the family land is seen in our story. It's a place of deep personal attachment, not a place that can be written off as a commodity that can be sold.

Yet Rachel's Tomb is situated in the center of Bethlehem, a large Palestinian city in the West Bank. Today, there is a security wall, built by the Israeli government, to separate the Palestinian territory of Bethlehem from the Israeli territory of Jerusalem. However, because Rachel's Tomb is situated inside Bethlehem, and because Israelis did not want to lose secure access to the tomb, the security wall is specially designed to reach inside the city center of Bethlehem and encircle the tomb, allowing Jewish Israelis to visit the site. It would be impossible for any Palestinian to understand the wall as anything other than a constant, ugly provocation.

This decision and design by the Israeli authorities in many ways represents the views of the wife in our story. The wife does not want to give up a place that is sacred and special to her, though practically it would make a lot of sense to do so. The wife, like the Israeli authorities, has chosen sacred history over practical current needs.

QUESTION FOR FURTHER EXPLORATION

- What sacred places within Israel, if any, would you be willing to give up for the sake of peace? What would you not be willing to give up? Why?

 ## THOUGHTS TO RETURN TO AFTER A NIGHT'S SLEEP

1. I wish I'd said ...

2. That idea I rejected, now that I think about it ...

3. That whole conversation reminded me of ...

"IF WE CAN SECURE a PLACE for argument, WE CAN FIND A SPACE for agreement."

– ALI ABU AWWAD

THE REFUGEE IN MY HOUSE

A neighbor has been made homeless. Should they take him in to their home?

COVID 19 hit us hard. It hit the entire neighborhood hard. Sari and I are just about making ends meet with online bits and pieces. The kids are going crazy, and, well, who am I kidding? We're all going crazy.

This morning it's getting even crazier. Sari's looking out the window and she's not moving. The cigarette in her hand is smoking itself. I join her. She's looking at Doron. Doron is our next-door neighbor. He's an actor. Or rather, he was before COVID. He's been out of a job for over a year and couldn't make his rental payments. So now he sleeps outside on our stoop.

Sari takes a toke of the cigarette and stubs it out decisively, saying, "That's it. I can't take it anymore. We have to invite him in. He's our neighbor. He needs a roof over his head. We should let him sleep on the couch."

"You have got to be kidding me!" I find myself saying before I have time to think. "First of all, he's not exactly our neighbor. He's a guy who used to live near us. We don't know him. We only found out he used to be an actor yesterday when we found him on the stoop. Second, we have our own problems! We can hardly feed ourselves, let alone someone else. It's not our problem."

"I just can't bear seeing him out there," wailed Sari.

"Neither can I. But I also can't bear the thought of waking up to him on the couch every morning! And what's going to happen with the kids? Which room will we homeschool them in? What kind of influence would he be? Will our kids be safe around this total stranger?"

Sari scowled at me.

"He's got nowhere else to go. He's an only child, and his parents are dead. The check from the government just got swallowed up by his debts. The homeless shelters are all full. And the hot winds of *sharav* are coming in."

"Sounds like you've been spending a whole lot of time thinking about this stranger and no time at all thinking about us. We're not a refugee center, and he's not a refugee"

Sari just looked at her watch.

"Forecast says that by lunchtime it'll be up to 100 degrees out there, and it's going to be the hottest summer ever."

 # GUIDING QUESTIONS

• Should the narrator agree to invite Doron in to live with them?

# BACKGROUND

A sharav is a period of hot, dry desert winds. In the summer in Israel temperatures can hit the 100s and stay there for a week. Without shelter or water, it is dangerous to be outside for long.

While the narrator argues that Doron is not a refugee, the reasons the narrator refuses shelter to Doron are very similar to the arguments offered by Israeli leaders who are against opening Israel's borders to African refugees. The narrator suggests Doron might be dangerous, might damage the family's home culture, and might place a strain on their limited resources.

Individuals from African countries, particularly Eritrea and Sudan, began to arrive in Israel in the early 2000s. Today there are about 36,000 African refugees living in Israel. Most of these individuals came to Israel seeking refuge, running away from the dangers of their home countries. Israel was not so quick to welcome them. A number of reasons were given for this. In South Tel Aviv, for example, where many Africans resided, the crime rate increased with their presence. Others felt that giving refuge to so many people would be too great a drain on an already strained economy, especially given the small size of the Israeli population. Still others felt that to keep the Jewish nature of the State of Israel, the country must limit the number of non-Jews who can immigrate.

While tens of thousands of Africans did make it in to Israel, the country has not made it easy for them to stay. A number of policies were created—and ultimately revoked—in order to deter additional immigration. These included taking a percentage of these immigrants' salaries, giving them residence but only in a prison, and at one point attempting to resettle a large number of these immigrants in different countries. As of late 2021 Israel has not begun a serious assessment of their asylum claims.

Some argue that Jewish tradition always reminds us to "welcome the stranger," and that since Europe made millions of Jews into refugees, Israel's response to refugees should be exemplary. Others argue that the huge wave of asylum seekers who would inevitably arrive if Israel became known as a safe haven would threaten Israel as a Jewish state.

 ## QUESTIONS FOR FURTHER EXPLORATION

• Should one be bound in the present by ancient principles?

• Is it moral to take care of strangers at the expense of your own family?

 ## THOUGHTS TO RETURN TO AFTER A NIGHT'S SLEEP

1 I wish I'd said …

2 That idea I rejected, now that I think about it …

3 That whole conversation reminded me of …

"HONEST DISAGREEMENT is often a GOOD SIGN OF PROGRESS."

— MAHATMA GANDHI

"As iron sharpens iron, SO ONE PERSON SHARPENS another."

- PROVERBS 27:17

THE SAMI LEVI NURSING HOME

> Should he agree to send his mother to the nursing home she so desperately needs, even if the act would lend legitimacy to the local gangster?

I knew Sami when he was a kid. I'm not sure if he knew me—maybe he recognized my face, but nothing more. I managed to remain beneath his radar. He never hit me or threatened me, and for kids in my neighborhood, that was already a success. As I grew up and moved away from my parents' house, I would occasionally hear reports of Sami's "progress." Thrown out of the army for beating up an officer, in prison for armed robbery, sought after for running some kind of protection racket.

I'd hear all his news from my mother, who would hear it from his. Whatever Sami's relationship was with the law, he always loved his mother, Ruhama. Her new plasma screen TV, the redo of her bathroom, the orthopedic bed— all gifts from Sami. If Ruhama had ever let him, Sami probably would have built her a palace at the seaside by now, but she refused to leave the neighborhood and her old friends.

His mother has seen better days. Her health is waning, and she's in need of constant care. We could all see, and Sami could see too, that she needed to move to some form of care home for the elderly. My mom would tell me how the garbage at Ruhama's place was full of glossy brochures advertising posh care homes that she'd thrown away the moment her son left the apartment.

135

She had no intention of leaving the neighborhood for a care home.

So Sami being Sami, he went for the direct approach. He built her a care home in the neighborhood itself. Within a year an entire apartment block "emptied itself out," was knocked down, and a brand-new superb elderly facility was built in its place. All the residents of the apartment block had sold to Sami and his friends. It's not known if they were offered a tidy sum of money or a concrete enough threat, but they cleared out pretty fast. A local counselor was particularly helpful in advancing municipal permissions (just as a new extension to his house miraculously appeared), and there was the horrible tale of an intransigent building inspector who had a terrible accident while attending to something on the top floor.

The Sami Levi Nursing Home opened its doors to the public last week. Sami proudly cut the ribbon, wearing a respectable suit and a cleanly shaven face. Word has it he is thinking of a career in politics. To be a generous benefactor of the best elderly care home in the country placed at the heart of a poverty-stricken neighborhood should do his prospects no harm.

His only issue is the residents. Apart from his mom, who was happily ensconced there from day one, no one else has moved in yet. There is a general unease with giving Big Sami Levi such a "kosher certificate." Sami can't use his usual persuasion tactics, either. First of all, the future residents of the Sami Levi Nursing Home are all his mother's best friends—God forbid if Ruhama Levi learned he'd ever done anything to harm them! And secondly, Sami knows that there is only one kind of person who is completely immune to his persuasion or threats—and that is an old person who doesn't want to leave their home.

I would love to have heard Mom's opinion on it all. But Mom doesn't really have an opinion on anything these days. Dementia swooped in all too quickly for my mom, like a dark curtain pulled closed. She needs 24/7 care. We tried to move her to a home, but she would wake up there every morning in a total panic. She'd leave the building and try to find her way back to the old neighborhood. Sometimes she'd get lost on the way, but sometimes we'd find her happily hanging out in her old park, babbling to old friends or young passersby or even some twittering birds. I gave up, and she's back in the old apartment.

I can't afford to pay for a live-in nurse any more. I'm doing okay, but I'm not a rich man. And anyway, the nurses never seem to last more than a few months, and then I have to leave work in the middle of the day and drive over an hour to look after Mom. The instability isn't good for her, and in her lucid moments she hates being a burden on me. She needs to be in a care home that's in the neighborhood.

She needs to move to the Sami Levi Nursing Home.

She's visited Ruhama there. She lights up to see her friend, and the fact that the view is of her favorite park—well, it's perfect. Sami has even offered a significant discount for people from the neighborhood. It's so hard to resist.

But if I move Mom into the Sami Levi Home, I know for sure that many families will follow suit. Everyone is waiting for the first domino to fall. Mom was always well-loved in the neighborhood. If people heard that Rivka Amsalem was moving in to Sami's home, that would mean a lot to them. It would give Sami the legitimacy that he's been looking for.

Sami Levi with even more power? With even more proof that his methods reap rewards? Using his money and his gangs even to take over politics in this place? How could I lend a hand to all that?

I don't know what to do.

GUIDING QUESTIONS

- Should he register his mother at the Sami Levi Nursing Home?

- What is more important, his mother's comfort and care, or his own conscience and the health of the society in which he lives?

CONTEXT

This story does not have roots in any true events. Israel is indeed challenged by organized crime, but it doesn't seem to be challenged any more, or in a more "Israeli" way than other countries. Corruption does exist in local and national government, as is evidenced by the number of mayors and ministers (and one prime minister!) who have gone to jail for corruption. Beyond this generic context, the details of the Sami Levi Nursing Home have no basis in fact.

We can provide some moral context, though.

We might see that this story is struggling with the commandment to honor one's mother and father on the one hand and the desire to avoid enhancing the reputation of an evil man.

Declared as one of the fundamental Ten Commandments is the insistence that we "Honor your father and your mother: that your days may be long in the land which the LORD your God is giving you." (Exodus 20:12). This commandment is repeated throughout the Jewish and Christian Bibles, and folktales warning against abandoning elderly parents appear throughout the world. Jewish, Caribbean, and Irish traditions all tell very similar morality tales against treating elderly parents badly. These days, as we live longer while our minds sometimes do not, the idea of placing an elderly parent in the care of professionals with 24/7 attention sometimes becomes an expression of love, not rejection.

It is clear to us that it would be good for the narrator's mother to find a place in a quality care home such as Sami Levi's.

On the other hand, the narrator knows that Sami Levi himself is a dangerous man whose reputation could be whitewashed by the success of the care home. A good reputation, or a "good name" is crucial in Jewish tradition. Rabbi Shimon said: "There are three crowns: the crown of Torah, the crown of priesthood, and the crown of royalty, but the crown of a good name supersedes them all." (Mishnah Avot 4:13)

The narrator is concerned about presenting Sami Levi with such a crown, and we might also guess he is concerned that his own and his mother's good name might be exploited and even darkened. Midrash Tanchuma on Parshat Vayakhel comes up with a deeply resonant aphorism:

"There are three names by which a person is called: one which their parents call them, one which people call them, and one which they earn for themselves. The last is the best one of all."

It might be that both the narrator and Sami Levi are concerned about all three of their names, concerned, as they are, for their mothers' welfare, their reputation in public, and the nature of their deeds.

QUESTIONS FOR FURTHER EXPLORATION

• What is the point of moral purity if it comes at the cost of a comfortable life for ourselves and our loved ones?

 ## THOUGHTS TO RETURN TO AFTER A NIGHT'S SLEEP

1 I wish I'd said ...

2 That idea I rejected, now that I think about it ...

3 That whole conversation reminded me of ...

"Be able to DEFEND YOUR ARGUMENTS IN A RATIONAL WAY. Otherwise, all you have IS AN OPINION."

— MARILYN VOS SAVANT

"You can't fight hatred with hatred and expect anyone to listen to you. You can only try to lessen it with humor, wit, truth, and common sense. If that doesn't work run like hell, while they throw rocks at you."

— Shannon L. Alder

Support Me

> A young Israeli soldier refuses to serve defending illegal outposts and begs his mother to support him in his clash with the army authorities, his friends, and his family.

"Leave me alone. I'm not getting up."

"You have to get up. You're going to be late!"

"I don't care. I'm never going back there. I'll serve the rest of my time in army prison. I don't care."

"No son of mine is going to refuse to serve in the Israel Defense Forces!"

"You're kidding, aren't you?" Alon sat up in bed now, gesturing animatedly. "Israel Defense Forces? I'm not defending Israel. I'm defending an outpost built on private Palestinian land that even Israeli law says is illegal. All the Jews there don't give a damn about Israeli law, and they spit on us soldiers. But we have to be there endangering ourselves, because they are Israeli citizens in danger of Palestinian attack. And why are they in danger of Palestinians? Because they're squatting on Palestinian land that they've stolen!"

He lay back down in bed, pulling up the covers again. "Israel Defense Forces—bull. I wish I was serving in the Israel Defense Forces. Let them put me in jail. I don't care."

"But don't you see that you're playing into the hands of the settlers? If you say it's okay to refuse army orders when you don't agree with them, that's exactly what they'll say. They'll point to people like you, and say, "Look. Even the lefties say it's okay to refuse orders you don't agree with. When the government sends the army to demolish the illegal Jewish settlements, they'll all refuse to do it—and say that you were the one who set the precedent.""

"Look, Mom, I'm doing this. I know what this means. I'm going to jail. They'll put me away for months if not more than a year. Don't think I'm cool with that. I'm terrified. I could really, really do with your blessing and your support."

"You know that I love you, Alon, and—"

"That's not what I mean," he said, cutting her off. "I mean your real support. Talk to Dad. Talk to Grandpa. Your friends. I'm not going to have the strength to go to jail if my whole family and neighbors are attacking me. Are you on my side or not?"

GUIDING QUESTIONS

- Are you on his side?

- When, if at all, is it okay or even preferable to break a law that conflicts with your values? When it is not okay?

- When, if at all, is "conscientious objection" a legitimate form of protest? If Alon had refused to serve in the army altogether (not just refused to act on a particular order), how, if at all, would that change your view?

BACKGROUND

In Israel there is mandatory army service for all eighteen-year-olds. Conscientious objection is a status that is protected, even in some ways more than a desire to stay safe. That is, an individual who is afraid to serve in the army because of the increased risk of dying will not be granted an exemption from army service. However, an individual who does not want to serve because of moral or ethical convictions—deeply held pacifist objections, for example— may be granted an exemption.

In Israeli law, however, there is a difference between holding general pacifist convictions and therefore refusing any army service, and holding a conviction against a particular duty within the army. In 2002 the Israeli High Court of Justice ruled that refusal to serve because of pacifism is legal, but "selective refusal," as they termed it, is illegal. Offenders are sent to jail. The High Court's official opinion is that refusing only certain assignments would "weaken the ties that bind us as a nation," and therefore is illegal.

On the mainstream left in Israel there is a general rejection of these "selective refusers." Some argue that if a left-leaning recruit does not serve, they will most likely be replaced by a less morally scrupulous soldier who would do more harm to Palestinian civilians. Others argue that if a left-leaning recruit refuses to serve, this lends legitimacy for right-leaning soldiers to refuse orders they reject as well.

The classic example of this was in 2005, when the army and the police were charged with evacuating Jewish settlements from Gaza. Right-leaning supporters of the Gazan settlers called on the soldiers—in particular the religious soldiers—to refuse to carry out their orders.

Doron is particularly concerned about his task in protecting an "illegal settlement." According to most international lawyers (but not most Israeli Jewish lawyers), all Jewish settlements over the Green Line, in what is known as the Occupied West Bank, are illegal. But within Israel there is seen to be a difference between settlements that were established by the state, with state resources and with state planning, and those settlements that were established in the face of state objections. These second kind of settlements are sometimes called "outposts" and are seen—even in Israel—as "illegal." However, even when living in "illegal outposts," these Israeli citizens are assigned soldier units to protect them from harm. Sometimes these residents reject the help of what they see as the establishment against which they are rebelling.

QUESTIONS FOR FURTHER EXPLORATION

• Should the Israeli army leave the "illegal" settlers without their defense?

• How can an army function if its soldiers obey only selectively?

 ## THOUGHTS TO RETURN TO AFTER A NIGHT'S SLEEP

1 I wish I'd said ...

2 That idea I rejected, now that I think about it ...

3 That whole conversation reminded me of ...

Should We Talk?

A Jewish Israeli and a Palestinian Israeli sit down for a silent yet full conversation over a cup of coffee in the Galilee.

I was down in Dir el Assad, picking up some materials. While the order was being put together, the owner of the workshop invited me for a coffee. Of course. And I accepted. Of course.

We weren't alone. Already sitting there, with one of those tiny coffee cups in his hand, was a friend of his. I'm guessing it was a friend of his. They were happily chatting away in Arabic, and it didn't look like the guy was waiting to buy anything. I found myself once again wishing my Arabic were better. My Arabic classes had been a disaster. It turns out that eventually one's brain fills up with languages and doesn't have room for any new ones. So I've got English, and I've got Hebrew. The French that used to be in my brain seems to have fallen off the shelf through lack of use or lack of room, and Arabic couldn't even get in the front door.

I'm used to smiling politely and drinking the coffee while others chatter in Arabic. There's no reason for me to expect they know Hebrew any better than I know Arabic, especially the older folks. But after a while I realize they're talking about me. They keep knocking glances over to me, and mentioning the name of my *kibbutz*: Tuval.

I politely ask what they're talking about.

The guest says, in broken Hebrew, "You from Tuval? My family used to own land there."

He smiles. I smile. We drink coffee in silence for a while.

My heart and head are flooded with questions I know I will never ask.

Did his family happily sell their land to my kibbutz, or was it somehow taken from them? Or was it an enforced purchase? As far as I know, most of the barren land on the top of our windswept mountain wasn't owned by anyone, and the rest was bought legally. But who knows?

Did his family really, officially, legally own land where my kibbutz stands? Or was this some kind of unspoken expectation within the village?

Did he spend his childhood summers playing around there with his cousins? Or does he have no memory of the place, only a family myth passed on from generation to generation?

Is he angry? Resigned? Resentful? At peace? Awaiting revenge?

And what questions does he have of me?

Does he wonder if I was innocently born on the kibbutz, or whether I made a conscious choice to live on the land his family had owned?

Does he ever expect me to leave my home so that he might return to his?

Does he think I don't care?

Does he ever wonder about the property that my grandparents fled from in Poland? And who lives there now?

Or does he, like me, believe that it would be too difficult, too dangerous to begin to find out the answers to any of these questions since no answer will bring about physical change, and so he, like me, smiles, and continues to drink his coffee with me in deep silence.

The coffee is thick, bitter, and generously sweetened.

 # GUIDING QUESTIONS

• Should they talk about the land and their relationship to it or not?

• What else should the narrator do or not do?

 # BACKGROUND

In 1917, when the superpower at the time, Britain, committed in the Balfour Declaration to a Jewish homeland in the area known as Palestine, Jews were around 6 percent of the population in that land. Locals could not understand how a homeland might be granted to those who are hardly present, without even consulting the majority of the people living there. In 1947 the UN agreed upon a partition plan which, taking into account the majority Arab population of the Galil area, designated most of the Galil to be part of the future Arab state. The Partition Plan was never implemented, and the entire area became part of the State of Israel. To this day, the Galil is 80 percent Arab Palestinian.

Much of the area, particularly along the Bet Hakerem Valley that runs between Akko and Tzfat, has Jewish communities peppered along the mountain ridges. These kibbutzim and community settlements were dubbed *mitzpim*, in the sense of "outlook spots" overlooking the Arab villages mostly located down in the valley. They were part of the government's plan to greatly increase the proportion of Jews living in the Galilee, termed "*Yihud HaGalil*—Judaization of the Galilee." In March 1976 the Israeli government announced the appropriation of some 20,000 dunams of land in the Galilee area, taking over at least 6,000 dunam of privately owned Arab land. This move was met with widespread protests and demonstrations that led to the death of four locals shot by the police and the army. On what came to be known as Land Day, hundreds were injured as 4,000 police, tanks, and armored vehicles entered the villages.

In addition to this painful legacy, the legalities of land ownership in the Galil are complex to say the least. Every town or village has a "perimeter plan" delineating how far outside the existing settlement the village can expand. According to traditions that predate the creation of the State of Israel, a village's perimeter is judged according to how far the voice of the *muezzin* (Muslim call to prayer) can be heard. If the muezzin is out of hearing, this is the outermost edge of the village. With the introduction of electronic loudspeakers for the muezzin, and the proliferation of mosques in some villages, what constitutes a village's land and what does not is an increasingly political decision. It is often the case that land that was not officially owned by anyone was seen to have been owned by someone despite there being no recognizable legal evidence.

Land Day is marked by locals every year. Yet it was over forty years ago. In this time the Jewish settlements that were established in its wake have reached their second, sometimes third generation. Many were born on their kibbutzim or moshavim, knowing no other place. In this strict sense, they are as native as the villagers who look at their birthplace as the site of a theft. In the meantime, throughout the Galil, and in the area of the story in particular, Jews and Arabs mingle freely, working with each other, buying from each other, and driving the same roads—often sharing a coffee or two.

 ## QUESTIONS FOR FURTHER EXPLORATION

- Have you ever avoided asking a crucial yet potentially painful question?

- Have you ever chosen to ask "that" question? Did you regret doing so, or were you pleased you had?

 ## THOUGHTS TO RETURN TO AFTER A NIGHT'S SLEEP

1   I wish I'd said ...

2   That idea I rejected, now that I think about it ...

3   That whole conversation reminded me of ...

I WAS BORN HERE

TRIGGER WARNING: References to violence.

A child is angry at their parents for choosing to continue living in a dangerous place.

From the moment I have known myself I have been afraid.

Not "frightened of the dark" kind of afraid, but afraid of death, murder, blood.

I remember when my uncle was shot while driving me to kindergarten. He kept driving, but there was so much blood. My schoolbag was stained, and my parents refused to buy me a new one. Out of principle. There was always a principle at stake in my home. Many ideologies and principles but none involved my safety or comfort.

My parents tell me it is our land. They tell me that we must never relinquish it, no matter how dangerous it is to live here. I think I understand. They tell me that we are at war with those who wish to take our land. Our enemies think that it is their land, not ours. I think I understand.

But I don't understand why our enemies want to hurt me.

I don't have a choice in all of this. My parents, my family, my society, they all insist I must stay here. But it wasn't my fault. I was born here. Sometimes I want to shout at them, as they block our way, shoot at my family, or throw things, "I was born here! I had no choice in your war! Leave me out of it!"

Last week my best friend was killed. He, too, was born here. He, too, had no choice.

I suddenly realized that I was no longer angry with his killers, I was angry with his parents. And with my parents.

Why do they choose to keep us in such danger?

Why can't we just run away from all this?

I want to live somewhere safe!

We have visas and money—we could live anywhere!

I awaited their return from the mourning house, ready to explode.

GUIDING QUESTIONS

- Would you advocate for the child to the parents, or would you support their choice to live in this dangerous place?

- When the narrator reaches an age when they can make their own decisions, would you advise them to leave or to stay?

- Are the parents wrong for putting their children in ongoing danger?

CONTEXT

This story is based on many real families who have made the decision to live in dangerous places, or in dangerous ways, for ideological reasons. Families, like the one in this story, may be Jewish or Palestinian. In both cases, the family likely believes that the land on which they live is theirs.

In Jewish families such as this one, their ideology may be a religious belief that God promised the land of Israel to the Jewish People, as is written in the Torah. Or, it may be a political ideology that understands the history of the wars of Israel, that the Israeli army fought and won the land in a war of defense. Families such as this one are afraid of Palestinian terror attacks. Often these families find themselves religiously and emotionally bound to the land, while also fearing the security threat that might arise from Arab enemies were they to forfeit the land.

In Palestinian families such as this one, their ideology may be one that is based on the narrative that connects them with their parents, grandparents, great-grandparents, and to the Palestinian People as a whole. They believe Jews wrested control over the land of the Palestinian People by force, and the Palestinians must never leave their land to grant victory to the Zionists. The story is often told with a physical key to the lock on the door of the house that once stood on their now dispossessed property. Most families (although not the one in this story) do not have anywhere else to move because of the political realities. These families are afraid of Israeli extremists and Israeli military who cause damage and injury.

In both cases, whether to the same or different extents, there are families who are fearful of attacks by the other side. In both cases, the decision to live where they live is ideologically charged.

 QUESTIONS FOR FURTHER EXPLORATION

- Do your opinions maintain the same level of clarity whether the child is Israeli-Jewish or Palestinian?

- Are parents right to make ideologically driven choices that put their children at risk?

- What is more important to you—your connection to a particular place or your physical safety?

THOUGHTS TO RETURN TO AFTER A NIGHT'S SLEEP

1 I wish I'd said ...

2 That idea I rejected, now that I think about it ...

3 That whole conversation reminded me of ...

"ELINOR AGREED TO IT ALL, FOR SHE DID NOT THINK he deserved the compliment of RATIONAL OPPOSITION."

- Jane Austen

Covid Wedding

She doesn't do vaccines. Ever. But when her twin sister insists on vaccines at her wedding, what is she to do?

Tali and I are the most twin-like twins there have ever been. Or at least that's what we like to tell everyone. All the identical twin tricks? We've done them. I've taken the rap for Tali's poor schoolwork, she broke up with my boyfriend for me, and we even contemplated sharing our army service half and half. We share everything. All our secrets, all our fears, all our dreams.

I knew she was going to marry Tomer before she knew. It was the way he knew how to differentiate between us the first time we met him. And the way she didn't even notice she'd spent a whole day with him without texting me once. I'm not at all jealous. It's funny the way the twin thing goes; however cute Tomer is, he really isn't my type. And I'm okay with spending less time with just me and Tali. We've always been good with giving each other space and having different friends.

Tali didn't need to announce the wedding to me. She just told me one evening, "You free on June 6 this coming year?" And the both of us just started whooping and dancing around. "I'm not going to be your dumb bridesmaid!" I screamed. "You're not going to be my stupid bridesmaid!" she screamed back. "It's best woman or nothing!"

"Totally!" And we danced some more.

So that was then. And this is now. Coronadays.

I'm sitting here with the e-invite to my twin sister's wedding. And it's there in black-and-white. "Entry only to guests carrying their own bottle of booze and their vaccination certificate!"

Tali knows what I think about her vaccine wedding. I thought she understood. I never get vaccinated for anything. She knows this. It was always our thing. When we toured the Far East together she got all the jabs, and I didn't. She gets the flu jab every year, and I don't. It's just who we are. If I'm honest about it, it's one of the ways we managed to stay two different people. She's always been the more conventional one, following the rules, trusting authority, and me—less so. Far less so.

I can't get vaccinated. The whole idea of it fills me with disgust and fear. I'll not bore you with what I think about how the whole world has invested in a vaccine instead of a cure, and how it's all useless unless the whole world gets a free vaccine because mutations will crop up as long as the virus is around. Forget that. Forget that we have no idea of the long-term effects of the vaccine. It's just not me. I am not that person. I do not get vaccinated. For anything. Ever.

But the invitation says it plain as plain can be.

How could I not be at Tali's wedding?

How could she get married without me?

Why is she doing this to me?

GUIDING QUESTIONS

- Which, if either of the sisters, should compromise?

- (When) Would you compromise on your deepest principles to celebrate with someone you love?

BACKGROUND

In Israel, in 2021, about a year into the COVID-19 pandemic, the Israeli government instituted special restrictions for gatherings, in an attempt to stem the spread of the illness. One of these restrictions was that large gatherings could only be held with participants who had a "green pass." Any person who has received two vaccines or who has recovered from COVID-19 automatically receives a green pass, as a sign that he or she is less likely to get and spread the illness.

In some cases, individuals or organizations decided to employ the concept of a green pass not only when the government required it, but as an extra health precaution, as in our story. For example, at different points during the pandemic, the government restricted indoor gatherings to green pass holders but allowed outdoor gatherings. And some individuals decided to enforce this rule for outdoor gatherings as well.

In addition, one is able to get a temporary green pass by taking a COVID-19 test and receiving a negative result before entering the gathering. In our story, it would seem that Tali decided not to allow for this option, as the invitation clearly stated being vaccinated as an entry requirement.

 ## QUESTIONS FOR FURTHER EXPLORATION

• If you were organizing a party, is it your responsibility to keep others safe, or is it the guests' own responsibility?

• When is safety more important than individual freedom, and when is freedom more important?

 ## THOUGHTS TO RETURN TO AFTER A NIGHT'S SLEEP

1 I wish I'd said ...

2 That idea I rejected, now that I think about it ...

3 That whole conversation reminded me of ...

About the Authors

Before getting into our respective resumes, you should know that Abigail Dauber Sterne and Robbie Gringras are very different people. Abi is a religious Orthodox Jew while Robbie is secular. Abi's mother is a successful businesswoman, whereas Robbie grew up in a socialist youth movement and lives on a kibbutz. Most crucially, Abi grew up in America, whereas Robbie hails from England. Disagreement has always been a way for us not only to improve and sharpen each other's work, but also as a way to become better colleagues and friends.

Abigail Dauber Sterne

Abigail Dauber Sterne has worked in the United States and in Israel as an educator and organizational leader for more than twenty years. Throughout her career, her focus has been on deepening people's Jewish experiences, while also promoting a deep pluralism. Through her roles in senior management at two international organizations—Hillel International and the Jewish Agency for Israel—she has relationships that span the globe. She has worked with rabbis, students, educators, and organizational leaders around the world.

Abi is a recipient of several fellowships in the Jewish communal world, including the Muehlstein Institute for Jewish Professional Leadership, the Tikvah Fellowship, and the Schusterman Fellowship. While continuing her work as an educator, Abi is now a rabbinical student at the Shalom Hartman Institute/HaMidrasha at Oranim, she has relationships with a wide network of leaders. She has spoken at many international conferences, and contributes opinion pieces to several online and print publications.

Abi lives in Jerusalem with her spouse and four children. Her family dinner table is always a raucous mixture of laughter and disagreement.

Robbie Gringras

Robbie Gringras has been an internationally renowned storyteller for the past thirty years and a global Israel educator for twenty, during which time he coined the "hugging and wrestling" approach to Israel engagement around the world. Graduating from Oxford University in English Language and Literature, he swiftly moved into professional theater. His work—both as a playwright and actor—has been performed on London's West End and in theaters throughout Europe, North America, Mexico, Hong Kong, Australasia, and Israel, in English, Spanish, and Hebrew. His unique style that combines storytelling, physicality, and theater has been behind eleven original theater productions that have performed in front of some 100,000 people.

Robbie also has a parallel career in international education, having spent two decades working with global Jewish education organizations. His innovations, teaching, op-ed writing, public speaking, and training have touched tens of thousands of Jews throughout the world. Robbie currently lives in the Galilee area of Israel with his wife and two kids.

Robbie views himself as terrible at arguments, but being in Israel has helped his education!

Appendix I

Abi's tips for leading a healthy argument with your family

If you're like my family, at the occasional family dinner—perhaps a Friday night or Shabbat meal—your table conversation goes something like this:

"How was school today?" I ask.

"Okay," Nina, my fourteen-year-old, answers.

"I'll tell you how school was," says my six-year-old, Dori. "My bum."

"Mom, did you sign the permission form already? You keep forgetting!" exclaims ten-year-old Annaelle.

And, twelve-year-old Yishai just sits with his nose in a book, not even looking up to take a bite of food.

After one too many meals with some version of this conversation, I desperately hope for something more stimulating—not just for the kids, but for me and my husband as well. So, on some occasions I've started to take out a story and read it aloud to try and shake things up. I've learned a lot from these impromptu story and argument sessions. Below are a few pointers to help make your conversations more meaningful, fun, and engaging.

1. Picking a story.

You might want to read ahead, so as to choose a story that's appropriate for your kids' ages. If you've got younger kids (below age ten), the "warm-up" stories are more accessible to them. Also, the allegorical stories work well, though they might not be able to participate as much in the conversation once you move to the deeper meaning of the story. If you're a family that hasn't discussed Israel much before, you might want to start with a "warm-up" story, even if you have older kids.

2. The setting.

When's the right time and place to do this? As noted above, I like the dinner table. We're all at the table anyway and often struggling to converse. But some families might enjoy doing this as a more planned activity. If you're planning a trip to Israel, for example, you may decide to engage with several of these stories, as part of your pre-trip education process. In either case, make sure you're all comfortable and can see one another. It's not a bad idea to have some snacks ready to munch on. Also, generally, I find the conversations work best after a lazy day, when we haven't had much to do or say to one another. It's as though the passions have been stored up and need to be put to good use.

3. Length of time needed.

This is really dependent on your family. Younger kids probably won't last more than ten to fifteen minutes. Older kids can usually stick to one story for about twenty minutes. And sometimes it's best to plan for two stories. Sometimes one story is of greater interest than another, and the second story may result in a better conversation than the first.

4. Facilitation.

A question we often ask ourselves is, how active a facilitator should I be? If you've got more vocal kids, sometimes they want to speak at once and can get frustrated when they can't respond right away. This generally takes some active facilitation. In my family with four kids, I sometimes need to list who will speak when, often allowing the younger kids, who find it harder to wait, to speak first. If you've got quiet kids, sometimes you may need to actively ask them an open-ended question, or prod them with a couple of additional ideas to get them talking. I recommend looking at the background page that goes with each story, and using some of the questions listed to get the conversation going. Whatever kind of family you've got, most important is that you allow the kids—and the adults—to engage with the idea. Don't fear a disagreement. In fact, if I see that most of us are agreeing, I try to take the opposing side, in an effort to help my kids see that there are other ways of seeing the world.

5. Screens & Technology.

Put them all aside. Ask everyone in the family, parents included, to turn off or remove all cell phones and screens from the room. Sure, you may feel that you can google some information that will help you with the conversation, but leave that for another time. All the information you need for a good conversation can be found in the "background" pages of each story. Googling even just one fact will actually end up as a distraction from having an in-depth conversation. So, we recommend putting it all aside. And, if you do have some additional information you're looking for, save it for later—and use the opportunity to have a follow-up conversation with your family another time.

Finally . . .

Perhaps the hardest part of a family conversation is that, as parents, most of us want our children to share the same views that we hold. This is not a bad thing in and of itself. But for the sake of these stories, see if you can genuinely let your kids try on different opinions. Consider helping them examine different sides—even ones with which you personally disagree. Try asking questions rather than giving answers. Try just putting out another piece of information that might challenge an idea. In the long run, we believe this will not only make them more critical thinkers, it will also make them more compassionate and able to listen to others.

APPENDIX II

Tips for leading a healthy argument with a group

Warm-up

By way of warm-up, ask participants to share the last time they had an argument that did not destroy the relationship, did not necessarily reach consensus, but led to some valuable learning nevertheless. (Label this as "a healthy argument.")

Depending on the size of the group, the sharing may be done in pairs or in small groups.

During the sharing, explore the nature of the relationship with the person they argued with. Was it close family? Close friends? Why might that be?

As you gather experiences, build with the group a "list" of qualities that a "healthy argument" entails. Perhaps listening? Passion but not anger? Honesty? Learning?

> Research has shown that disagreements are far more inventive, rich, and generative when the interlocutors have read an article that demonstrates nuance and openness to other opinions. This kind of "priming" is going on in the conversation about "healthy arguments."

Presenting the story

If you are using a story with a video animation, make sure the screening is of a high quality and that everyone can hear. If you are working from a written story, we would recommend choosing an excellent reader—even yourself.

> Presentation of the story must be as engaging as possible. Do not use the reading of the story as an opportunity for addressing group dynamics—now the focus must be on the text itself.

Immediate responses

Each story leaves one with a "side" to take. Before having any conversations, ask the group to vote. Make the choice a binary: for or against. Reassure everyone that this is a temporary straw poll and that everyone is fully invited to change their minds later on if they want.

> Two messages here:
> First of all, no one is allowed to sit this one out. Even if they don't express their reasons, they must commit themselves to an opinion.
> Second, if you are about to split into smaller groups, you want to ensure that each group has people with differing views; otherwise things might get kind of dull.
> If you find that everyone is agreeing with only one side, you will need to invite people to "try on" a perspective they disagree with, for the sake of the exercise.

Opening round

You might wish to share a text copy of the story, and allow time for everyone to read it once again. Check that everyone has understood what happened in the story.

Begin by asking each person in the group which side they voted for, and, if applicable, *which part of themselves they would like to apologize to, for taking this stance.*

One clear concern for a participant at the opening of these kinds of exercises is that they will be socially judged and sentenced according to their stance. This exercise allows all to signal: "I take this particular stance, but it does not symbolize everything I am." It also allows all to hear and internalize that we all tend to be less morally and ideologically consistent than we might wish—and that's okay.

Facilitating the argument

Here you may need to work against your instincts or experience. Your role is not to smooth things out, nor to help people avoid conflict. It's pretty much the opposite. If you feel you need to intervene nevertheless, we would recommend that, rather than looking to offer ways around a conflict, you could offer deeper ways to dig into it by looking for the underlying values clash.

For example: "Beyond the rights and wrongs of whether a captain should or should not sing the national anthem, would it be fair to say that you two don't agree on the value of national symbols altogether?"

Debriefing the experience

On their own, in silence, ask all participants to write down two things: 1) What points were being made by those I disagreed with? 2) What is my opinion now?

It's good practice to give pride of place to the points of those you disagree with. It gives them respect even if you disagree with them, it enables you to remember why others may disagree with you in the future, and it reminds you that there are other opinions that you might find yourself adopting in the future.

Allow space for participants to talk about their frustrations, their discomfort, or their reticence. Assure everyone that we don't become experts at healthy arguments overnight. Draw out areas that left participants feeling stronger, wiser, curious—we want them to want more!

If you have time, invite participants into the philosophy behind this project of For the Sake of Argument. Share the vision of engaging with the world instead of retreating into our camps. See if the vision resonates with them.

Mark of success: Participants would like to do it again...

The next day . . .

If you are in contact with the participants the day after the argument, you might wish to follow up with the three guiding questions we have placed at the end of each story.

The nature of our opinions is that they are not fixed. Our identity does not fall or stand on our opinions. The more we practice noticing how our thinking can change, how our opinions are "hypotheses" to be tested, the more likely we are to be able to grow through disagreement.

Appendix III

Discussing the Four Arguments of Hope

> Alex and Jamie get into a conversation about what is important to argue about when arguing about Israel.

What makes for a "worthwhile" argument about Israel?

ALEX: Getting people to argue about Israel is easy. The challenge is getting them to argue about things that are worth arguing about.

JAMIE: What do you mean "worth" arguing about?

ALEX: I mean that arguing takes effort. There's no point wasting all that time and effort on pointless stuff.

JAMIE: And who are you to say what is pointless? Sounds pretty elitist, to me.

ALEX: Ha! Okay, let me try it a less elitist way then! Have you ever been in a conversation or disagreement about Israel and left it feeling that you were talking at totally cross-purposes?

JAMIE: Nearly all the time . . .

ALEX: And have you ever found yourself arguing about an Israeli issue that, when it comes down to it, isn't really about Israel at all?

JAMIE: What do you mean?

ALEX: Well, sometimes I get into arguments about Israel, but I realize underneath it all we're actually talking about American politics and using Israel as a kind of illustration.

JAMIE: Yes, totally!

ALEX: Or sometimes my friend and I begin talking about Israel, but in the end find we're just talking about ourselves and our own issues and feelings.

JAMIE: What's wrong with talking about your own feelings? Isn't it good that we bring our whole selves into the conversation?

ALEX: Of course. I'm not sure we could keep our whole selves out of a conversation about Israel even if we wanted to. But I just mean that sometimes a disagreement about Israel leads away from Israel itself and ends up being only about the people in the room.

JAMIE: I still don't understand what's wrong with that.

ALEX: Oh, I get what you mean. No, there is nothing at all wrong with that. That would be a healthy and important conversation to have. But . . .

JAMIE: But?

ALEX: But I'm not sure that anyone would be any the wiser about Israel.

JAMIE: But I think it's really valuable to talk through what is meaningful for everyone in the room. Even if it doesn't concern Israel.

ALEX: Me too. It's massively valuable. And at the same time, I think there is also huge educational value in disagreements about Israel and Israeli issues themselves. Where we bring our whole selves, opinions and emotions and all, into a conversation about something that is uniquely or fundamentally about Israel.

JAMIE: Okay.

ALEX: So that's what I meant by "something that's worth arguing over."

JAMIE: An argument that enables us to grow in our relationship with and understanding of Israel.

ALEX: Right!

JAMIE: Don't know why you didn't just say that . . .

ALEX: I . . . you . . . never mind. So we're looking for the kinds of arguments, the kinds of issues that enable us to grow in our relationship with and understanding of Israel.

JAMIE: Now I'm with you.

ALEX: And I'm not talking about how we talk to each other, okay? I'm assuming we're not throwing chairs at each other too much while we argue.

JAMIE: Good assumption.

ALEX: So less about "how" we argue, and more about "what?"

JAMIE: Go on.

ALEX: So I'd say we're looking for arguments that are deep and ongoing. Arguments that don't have easy or logical conclusions.

JAMIE: As an educator, perhaps I'd say they need to hinge on an "essential question?"

ALEX: Sounds good . . . what is an essential question?

JAMIE: An open-ended question about something that can't be answered through a google search. It's a thought-provoking question that the learner keeps coming back to over the years.

ALEX: Yes, that works. Your "essential question" kind of parallels what Jewish tradition calls an "argument for the sake of heaven." An argument that addresses eternal questions, that we engage in so as to gain wisdom rather than power.

JAMIE: That fits.

Finding inquisitive energy

ALEX: Okay! So ideally these arguments would be about the deep underlying principles that lie at the heart of the Zionist enterprise.

JAMIE: Now there's a phrase that already invites an argument!

ALEX: Ha! True! But at the same time as dealing with Zionist principles, these arguments would also embrace deep underlying principles at the heart of what's going on in the world. We need to find the arguments about Israel that also inform broader aspects of our lives.

JAMIE: Let me guess. You have some suggestions ready on hand?

ALEX: I'll bet you do too. No one is listening—why don't you throw out the most contentious, most troubling issues in the world that gain added heat when applied to Israel?

JAMIE: What, for real?

ALEX: I dare you.

JAMIE: Okay, well . . . sometimes there's a kind of feeling that Zionism is kind of more on the side of—

ALEX: Come on, forget the euphemisms for a second!

JAMIE: All right then . . . racism!

ALEX: Yes! That's definitely an issue that is troubling and gains heat when applied to Israel. More!

JAMIE: Nationalism.

ALEX: Yes. And?

JAMIE: Settler colonialism. Human rights. Indigeneity. Intersectionality. Anti-Semitism. Immigration. Refugees. War . . .

ALEX: Now you've got the idea!

JAMIE: I've only just gotten started.

ALEX: I'm sure!

JAMIE: You're not going to publish this list anywhere?

ALEX: Why not?

JAMIE: I'd get fired! And besides, you only asked for the troubling stuff. It's not a list of everything that Israel means to me.

ALEX: I get it. Don't worry. We'll publish this anonymously.

JAMIE: Okay. But honestly. It's not all I think about Israel.

ALEX: I know. But let's agree that you've given us a list of a whole load of topics that lots of us—especially learners—want to talk about, and lots of us—especially educators—would be happy to avoid!

JAMIE: Without a doubt.

ALEX: It's a list of combustible topics.

JAMIE: Right.

ALEX: They could burn the whole house down. But, just imagine the inquisitive energy we might release if we were able to harness this heat constructively.

JAMIE: Inquisitive energy. I like that.

The technical, the emotional, and the cognitive

ALEX: So we have to come at it from three directions to make sure it brings heat and not destruction. Some of our work has to be a kind of technical work. We have to practice how to listen, how to give space, how to acknowledge differences respectfully. To an extent, these are skills that can be taught.

JAMIE: Sure.

ALEX: Then there's the emotional work. We have to practice being in an argument and living with that discomfort we generally try to avoid.

JAMIE: I hate that. I run a mile from arguments usually.

ALEX: Most of us do. But nowadays that leads us to stay stuck in our like-minded social media bubbles, while the world splits into narrow, polarized pieces.

JAMIE: I know. I have to get braver.

ALEX: It's not easy. It's about building our emotional muscles. *Stories for the Sake of Argument* is your workout guide!

JAMIE: I'm ready!

ALEX: We need the third direction too. If we're going to invest time and effort in learning new skills and in building up our emotional resilience, we also need to prepare our brains.

JAMIE: What for? To protect our brains from exploding when we hear something dumb?

ALEX: To find the togetherness in our disagreement.

JAMIE: The what in the which?

ALEX: We need to prepare our brains to be clear about what it is we are arguing over. If we manage to do that, we might find that the person we're talking to is not an idiot nor evil but simply sees a different—

JAMIE: Wrong . . .

ALEX: Different solution to our shared problem.

JAMIE: Someone hates the Occupation. Someone else supports it. In what way is that a shared problem?

ALEX: It's all about families.

JAMIE: Families?

ALEX: Families of disagreement.

JAMIE: Here we go . . .

ALEX: No, seriously. There are four "families" of disagreement about Israel, four areas of concern that we argue about. And they cover all the combustible items you listed earlier and many more besides.

JAMIE: Only four? I can't believe that.

ALEX: I didn't say there are only four arguments. I just said that all the arguments can be understood as living in four fairly distinct families. And the more aware we are of these four families of argument, and of how they interact with one another, the more capable we will be of living with and learning from our disagreements.

JAMIE: Now you're moving from elitist to fantasist.

ALEX: Perhaps. Perhaps not.

JAMIE: Four "families," you say?

ALEX: Yes. Want to hear more about them?

JAMIE: What are they, these four families of argument of yours?

The Four Families of Argument:

1) Security

ALEX: Let's start with security. In Israel there's been an ongoing argument that began even before the creation of the state about life and death. It's an argument about the best way to keep safe.

JAMIE: Isn't that for the army to decide?

ALEX: But even they argue! Should we have more defensive systems like the Iron Dome? Or should we engage in more preemptive strikes with evermore sophisticated warheads? Then-Defense Minister Peretz had to fight tooth and nail for the army to develop the Iron Dome.

JAMIE: But he was doing that as a civilian, wasn't he?

ALEX: Exactly. From early in the state's existence, civilians got involved, arguing that withdrawing from places such as the Sinai in exchange for peace with Egypt would be better at ensuring our security than facing down their enmity. Some insisted that Palestinian terrorism might end if we were to enable them to have their own state alongside Israel.

JAMIE: Some still do insist.

ALEX: Exactly. Deep arguments go on for ages. And anyway, these days, security, issues of life and death are argued more with the medical community than the military.

JAMIE: What do you mean?

ALEX: COVID-19.

JAMIE: Ah. How could I forget . . .

ALEX: Should we wear more masks or keep more distance? Should we shut down or open up? When? Where? All these are also arguments in the family of security.

JAMIE: Okay, but I still don't get how this "family" idea leads us to your 'togetherness in arguing' thing.

ALEX: Togetherness in disagreement.

JAMIE: Yes, that.

ALEX: Okay, let's look at the suggestion in the US that schoolteachers should be trained in arms use.

JAMIE: Don't get me started.

ALEX: No, listen. Agree or disagree, they are positing an answer to the question, how can we keep our kids safe?

JAMIE: A really, really dumb answer.

ALEX: Perhaps. I'm guessing your answer would have more to do with making sure no one should have guns, right?

JAMIE: Pretty much.

ALEX: So both of you are in the same argument family. Both of you say you want there to be greater security. But you disagree about the solution to this problem.

JAMIE: Vehemently.

ALEX: Sure. But here's the chink of light. Both of you wish for greater security. You share a concern. That's why you're arguing. You disagree vehemently about the solution to the same problem.

JAMIE: Hmm.

ALEX: Togetherness in disagreement.

JAMIE: Hmm.

ALEX: Completely convinced, huh?

JAMIE: What's the second family?

The Four Families of Argument:

2) Collective Identity

ALEX: The second family is about collective identity. In America, we might talk about what it means to be American. In Israel, the argument is about what it means to be Jewish.

JAMIE: That's apples and oranges. American is a nationality. Judaism is a religion.

ALEX: Not for Israel. Or at least for Israel it's not only a religion.

JAMIE: Oh boy.

ALEX: Take a look at Israel's Declaration of Independence and look for the word "religion" or "faith." Or even "God," for that matter.

JAMIE: Not there?

ALEX: The word used throughout is "People" or "Nation." The State of Israel was established for and by the Jewish People, not for the Jewish religion.

JAMIE: What does that mean, though?

ALEX: It means a whopping great argument, that's what it means.

JAMIE: Figures.

ALEX: The Jewish People is a combination, or a tension, between the Jewish religion, Jewish solidarity, and the way Jews contribute or interact with the world.

JAMIE: What's that last one?

ALEX: Ever heard of "Jewish values?"

JAMIE: Of course.

ALEX: It's that. The way Jews apply their values beyond their own community.

JAMIE: So religion, solidarity, and values?

ALEX: Complete harmony, right?

JAMIE: I'm no expert in Israel, but I know that the way the religion is playing out there is one big mess.

ALEX: A big argument. Exactly.

JAMIE: All the religious are taking over, right?

ALEX: There's definitely an argument about it. Though it's not clear who's winning it. There's some excellent research by Camil Fuchs and Shmuel Rosner that shows that secular Jews believe there is too much religious coercion, while Orthodox Jews in Israel believe there is too much secular coercion!

JAMIE: And who is right?

ALEX: Depends what we mean by religious and secular coercion. It's an ongoing argument.

JAMIE: And what about that solidarity aspect of collective identity? Isn't it just a nice word for preferring your group above others'?

ALEX: Is that wrong?

JAMIE: Of course it is. All this looking out for Jews, isn't it just plain racism?

ALEX: Harsh . . .

JAMIE: Perhaps. But isn't it?

ALEX: I think you're pointing to one of the biggest arguments in this family of collective identity. Is it possible to look after "us" without denigrating everyone "else?" How should we choose between looking after "us" and looking after "all?"

JAMIE: Why should we choose?

ALEX: Good question. I guess sometimes we have to.

JAMIE: Why?

ALEX: Here you go. A real-world example. Israel moved swiftly to acquire COVID-19 vaccinations. After vaccinating its own population in early 2021, it has a few million spare shots that might as well be used by someone before they expire. Who should Israel send them to?

JAMIE: The Palestinians.

ALEX: That's one option, for sure. Israel could send the vaccines to all Palestinians in the West Bank and Gaza, since the Palestinian Israeli citizens were of course already eligible for vaccinations. But hang on a minute. What about all the Jews around the world who had no access to the vaccine, either? At the time there were no vaccines in Australia, Brazil, South Africa. Why shouldn't Israel instead send vaccines to the Jewish communities there?

JAMIE: That would be—

ALEX: Or for that matter, why send them to one group at all? Shouldn't Israel send the vaccines to the WHO, not to the Palestinians, and not to the Jews, but to the world?

JAMIE: I just think that—

ALEX: Want to argue about it?

JAMIE: Yes, I uh … Ah! I see what you're doing.

ALEX: All these arguments about Jews' relationships with the rest of the world, about our solidarity with each other, and about what is sacred for us—all these are arguments in the family of collective identity.

JAMIE: Okay, I can get that. Although I don't see how all these esoteric arguments are relevant to anyone who isn't Israeli or Jewish.

ALEX: Really?

JAMIE: Really.

ALEX: So why did it matter that the American withdrawal from Afghanistan left behind hundreds of Green Card holders?

JAMIE: Because—

ALEX: What is the difference between someone with a Green Card who wants to get away from Taliban rule, and someone who is just plain Afghani?

JAMIE: For me there is no difference. They're all human beings.

ALEX: And if you don't have room on the plane for everyone, and have to choose nevertheless? Five hundred US citizens, or five hundred Afghanis?

JAMIE: What's your point?

ALEX: My point is that collective identity is a family of arguments that applies to us all. And that's even before mentioning ideas like "America First" or the defiled sanctity of the House of Congress.

JAMIE: Okay, okay, so it is relevant to America too. What's your third argument family?

The Four Families of Argument:

3) Freedom

ALEX: Freedom!

JAMIE: Why should freedom be an argument?

ALEX: You're asking me this from the United States in the year 2021? In a period where the results of the presidential election are still being questioned by millions of people? And where there is a raging argument about the freedom of people to go without masking their faces? Freedom contains a huge family of arguments.

JAMIE: Go on.

ALEX: Look, all democracies face a built-in tension. You might even call it a built-in argument.

JAMIE: You are enjoying yourself, aren't you?

ALEX: Look at it. It's built-in. The majority are free to make choices for everyone that might infringe on the freedom of the individual to make choices. Like whether or not to put on a mask. Or a helmet. Or a safety belt. Or to smoke in offices. Or to have an abortion. And so on.

JAMIE: And Israel? That's the argument in Israel?

ALEX: It's one of them. We also had our lockdowns over the pandemic. But we might say that there are even more significant arguments over freedom in our part of the world. Look, it's no secret that Israel's armed forces see that the way to defend Israel is by maintaining control over a few million Palestinians over the Green Line. And it's also no secret that these Palestinians have no vote over the soldiers' mission, while Jews living in the same area do have that vote. Can we argue about this?

JAMIE: I'd say we probably can!

ALEX: Does this significant flaw at the heart of Israel's current democracy mean that it is not a democracy at all?

JAMIE: As far as I'm concerned . . . well, let's say I'm concerned.

ALEX: And what might you do with someone who is completely fine with this situation?

JAMIE: Argue.

ALEX: Right.

JAMIE: So we've covered three families of argument. Security, freedom, what was the second one?

ALEX: Collective identity.

JAMIE: Got to be a more catchy way of putting it.

ALEX: There is. But first let's cover the final argument family.

JAMIE: Which is?

The Four Families of Argument:

4) Territory

ALEX: Territory.

JAMIE: What?

ALEX: Arguments over territory.

JAMIE: What is this, the Treaty of Westphalia?

ALEX: The what?

JAMIE: I don't know. Some ancient treaty that stuck in my head from history class.

ALEX: You think this is old-fashioned? It's the most pressing family of arguments there is.

JAMIE: Convince me.

ALEX: Who says that your nation owns a particular piece of land? That border you share with Mexico—who put it there, and who decides who and what is allowed to cross it?

JAMIE: I seem to remember our last president had a lot to say about it.

ALEX: Every president has had a lot to say about it. Some of them say it quietly, some of them say it louder. Some of them you want to disagree with, and some you don't. But they are all very careful about what and who can cross their borders.

JAMIE: I suppose so . . .

ALEX: We disagree about territory more and more. We are living through the worst refugee crisis in a century. Millions of people are looking to cross borders, to leave what was their territory and live in the territory of others.

JAMIE: Especially with the climate crisis.

ALEX: Another argument over territory!

JAMIE: What is?

ALEX: The climate crisis. What good does it do if the United States or Canada cut the carbon emissions in their territory if all the rain forests in the territory of Brazil are being burned down?

JAMIE: We all have different countries and all live on one interconnected planet.

ALEX: And there's one big argument right there.

JAMIE: Depressing.

ALEX: So let's cheer you up and look at how this family of arguments applies to Israel!

JAMIE: Wait! I think I can do this now.

ALEX: Go ahead.

JAMIE: So in Israel there is a territory where not only two nations claim indigeneity, but also three religions.

ALEX: Yup. Not just a political territory but also a Holy Land.

JAMIE: And it's a territory lacking internationally recognized borders in the North and East.

ALEX: Add to that, think about how the most important areas in biblical Israel—Hebron, Bethel, the Temple Mount in Jerusalem—are all outside the internationally recognized borders of the State of Israel.

JAMIE: But also that the whole territory of the state was effectively conquered by force. So that pretty much undermines Israel's moral claim over the territory altogether.

ALEX: I suppose it would, if there was ever a time throughout history that the Holy Land was not taken through force of arms?

JAMIE: True . . . there *were* the Ottomans. And the Mamelukes, Salah ad Din . . .

ALEX: The Crusaders, Romans . . . it goes on forever. So what makes it "our" territory?

JAMIE: An argument?

ALEX: Or more often, a war.

JAMIE: Okay, that's the fourth family of arguments.
           One: security, two: um . . .

ALEX: Collective identity!

JAMIE: Right, that, and then freedom and then territory. You told me there was a catchier way of remembering them.

Overlapping Arguments of Hope

ALEX: There is. Four words in Hebrew. Four words that roughly map on to the four families.

JAMIE: Oh, come on. I hardly know any Hebrew, how's that going to help?

ALEX: I'm going to bet that these four words are familiar to you. I'll give them to you first in their English translation.

JAMIE: Wise move.

ALEX: The way to remember security, collective identity, freedom, and territory is through the Hebrew line: To be a People free in our land.

JAMIE: Hang on, that *is* familiar . . .

ALEX: And in Hebrew – *Lihiyot am chofshi b'Artzenu.*

JAMIE: Wait a minute, that's from, that's from—

ALEX: The Israeli national anthem, "Hatikva," the Hope. It's the penultimate line. I bet they made you sing it at some Israeli Independence Day celebration once.

JAMIE: More than once!

ALEX: *Lihiyot*—to be—is about security. About to be or not to be. *Am*—people or nation—is about collective identity.

JAMIE: Yes! Much easier to remember!

ALEX: *Chofshi*—free

JAMIE: Explains itself.

ALEX: And *b'Artzenu*—in our land—sums up the family of arguments around ownership of or connection to territory.

JAMIE: It's nice.

ALEX: Thank you.

JAMIE: It fits neatly.

ALEX: Uh-huh.

JAMIE: I think I like it.

ALEX: But?

JAMIE: I said I like it!

ALEX: You said you *think* you like it.

JAMIE: I do.

ALEX: You're not convinced.

JAMIE: It's just that . . .

ALEX: Come on then . . .

JAMIE: It's just that life happens in sentences, not in single words.

ALEX: I'm sorry?

JAMIE: I mean you've drawn some really elegant issues. Each of the four standing alone. Four different words.

ALEX: Four families of argument.

JAMIE: Right. But they can't stand alone. They affect one another. They interlock.

ALEX: True.

JAMIE: I mean, the intersection between arguments over peoplehood (People) and of democracy (freedom) is inescapable.

ALEX: Go on.

JAMIE: Well, before you talk about majorities and minorities, you have to agree on who you are allowing to vote and who you aren't. Who is in your "People" and who isn't?

ALEX: The "demos" bit in democracy.

JAMIE: The what in the which?

ALEX: Never mind. Keep going. You're on a roll.

JAMIE: Okay, another overlap. Before Zionism, the Jews were the ever-fleeing People. Somewhere is dangerous, they run away to the next place. According to your argument families, when their safety is at stake, Jews would give up on territory.

ALEX: Bye-bye, Anatevka.

JAMIE: What?

ALEX: Never mind.

JAMIE: But then come the Zionists, and the stand at Tel Chai, and
           suddenly we're saying that instead of running away from danger,
           we're going to stay put in one place and fight, even if that is
           dangerous.

ALEX: A complete paradigm shift.

JAMIE: Security and territory, "to be" and "in our land", aren't two
           separate arguments. They overlap.

ALEX: And no more so when we argue over the conflict with the
           Palestinians. Then we're disagreeing across all four families at
           once. Security issues overlap with issues of collective identity,
           which spill into questions of freedoms and democracy, which are
           inextricably bound up with control over territory.

JAMIE: To say nothing of the need for the Palestinians themselves to
           have their own arguments over their desire "to be the Palestinian
           People, free, in the land of Palestine" (which happens also to be
           the land of Israel.)

ALEX: You've got it!

JAMIE: I know I have. But how does it help?

ALEX: So now we're back to what is worth arguing about.

JAMIE: I guess so.

ALEX: Can we first agree that in order to have a worthwhile argument about Israel, it should live somewhere within these four families?

JAMIE: Yes. They're at the center of it all.

ALEX: I agree. So to begin with, they allow us to do some sifting. To make some choices about what we should include in our "Israel argument canon," and what is peripheral.

JAMIE: I still don't like "peripheral," but I get that these four are at the heart of it all.

ALEX: Next, using these "four families," we can sometimes hone in on what we're actually arguing about and what we're not. Women of the Wall, for example. Some people will argue that women should be allowed to pray where and how they want, because it's a fundamental human right. Others will argue that these women are damaging the unity of the Jews by praying at the Kotel in their non-Orthodox way.

JAMIE: Ah, I get it! The first group are talking about freedom, and the second group are talking about People.

ALEX: Right. So is it any wonder that both sides will feel like they're talking at cross-purposes?

JAMIE: Because they are.

ALEX: Yup! And then there's the idea that might also give us some hope.

JAMIE: Like in the "Hatikvah"–the Hope, in the Israeli national anthem?

ALEX: I personally think that there's something hopeful in realizing
           we care about the same things, even if we don't agree on what
           we ought to do about them. The arguments over security are
           because we all want "To Be." We argue about issues of Jewish
           Peoplehood or collective identity, because they are important to
           all those who argue. All our arguments about Israel, the ongoing
           struggle "to be a People free in our land," all these arguments
           emerge because we have a shared family of four major concerns.

JAMIE: This is your togetherness in disagreement thing, isn't it?

ALEX: It is. When we're bound up in a terrible argument, we forget our
           common ground. This way of listening out for the four Hebrew
           words, for the four ideas of Zionism, allows us to stay aware of
           our togetherness even when in disagreement. It provides us with
           some space in our minds and our hearts.

JAMIE: Okay.

ALEX: Which is why the specifically "Israel" stories in this book all live
           inside the four argument families of "Hatikvah." For example—

JAMIE: Wait, let me have a go. "The Good Man." Definitely about People—
           the way he understands his Judaism, and the way he's trying to
           help all people.

ALEX: Sure. And freedom definitely plays in there too.

JAMIE: Women's freedom. Yes, of course.

ALEX: What about "The King of the Travelers?"

JAMIE: Well, it's definitely about land. In fact, it's all about what enables us to call some territory "our land."

ALEX: And?

JAMIE: And it's about security. Not having some goon threaten to beat you up if you don't give him your land.

ALEX: Any other stories about "to be," and "in our land?"

JAMIE: Oh wow, there's that heart-wrenching one about the child who wishes their parents would move somewhere safer.

ALEX: "I Was Born Here," yes.

JAMIE: But some of the stories don't have anything to do with Israel. Like "Musica Cubana." That's about Cubans in Florida.

ALEX: Well, it is and it isn't. It's still in the same family of arguments.

JAMIE: In what way?

ALEX: All arguments about democracy are a combination of two argument families. They're about freedom, and they're about collective identity. Who gets to be the "us" that has the right—the freedom—to change the reality for "us?"

JAMIE: I suppose in that sense then, "That's The Way It Is" is also about freedom and People.

ALEX: I suppose it is.

JAMIE: To be a People free in our land. Hmm. Four arguments in one sentence.

ALEX: A sentence that we sing in hope . . .

JAMIE: Good luck to us all!

APPENDIX IV

About For the Sake of Argument:
the project.

For the Sake of Argument is an innovative educational project aimed at harnessing the energy and interactivity of live disagreement for the health of the Jewish People in general and Israel engagement in particular. We operate along three main drivers of activity.

The first driver is the publication of this book. *Stories for the Sake of Argument* contains twenty-four short stories designed to provoke disagreements about issues central to the State of Israel and the Jewish world. The stories are crafted to lead to a dilemma that must be addressed, and are accompanied by guiding questions, background material, and additional activities to be completed online.

The second driver is in the creation of "argument circles." For the Sake of Argument has a pool of trained facilitators who you can hire to run arguments, using materials from the book. At the same time, For the Sake of Argument runs training sessions for organizations, to prepare their staff to run their own argument circles and to work with the materials. We also advise educational organizations on ways to introduce the stories and their arguments into their curriculum.

The third driver is in the development and dissemination of a new pedagogy of argument. We believe that Israel education should aim for the learner to acquire the information, the emotional stamina, and the confidence to have healthy arguments about Israel and Israel's issues. We are developing an educational strategy that will allow learners to take their own stand in arguments about Israel and Israel's issues—a stand they have chosen through exploration—and continue to explore.

If you want to know more about any aspect of our work, please visit us at forthesakeofargument.org